Morton Beahner

The Problem of Induction

and Its Solution

The Problem of Induction and Its Solution

Jerrold J. Katz

The University of Chicago Press
Chicago and London

Library of Congress Catalog Card Number: 62-18116

THE UNIVERSITY OF CHICAGO PRESS, CHICAGO 60637
The University of Chicago Press, Ltd., London W.C. 1

Die Alten sind allerdings insofern klarer,
als sie einen klaren Abschluss anerkennen,
während es bei dem neuen System scheinen soll,
als sei a l l e s erklärt.

WITTGENSTEIN, *Tractatus*, 6. 372

To my mother
Lillian Katz

Preface

The present book offers a solution to the problem of induction, one of the standard problems in modern philosophy. This problem, which originated with the eighteenth-century philosopher David Hume, is, in the broadest sense, that of furnishing adequate grounds for justifying the principle of induction, the rule we use to make inferences about unknown events from a sample of data drawn from experience. The problem thus formulated includes the question of how we know past experience is a reliable basis on which to predict the future, which is the form the problem took when first posed by Hume.

There are three ways to approach the problem of induction, and each represents an influential viewpoint in contemporary philosophical thought. First, one can attempt to construct a justification for induction. Second, one can try to show that there is no genuine problem of justifying induction because the problem rests on a conceptual confusion about the nature of induction or the nature of justification. Advocates of this viewpoint argue that a solution to the problem of induction consists in showing that a justification is unnecessary. They argue that a solution is nothing but the exhibition of the conceptual confusion which first led philosophers to seek a justification of induction. Third, one can try to show that no justification of induction is possible. The present book takes this latter approach and offers a proof to show that there can be no argument which is capable of fulfilling the conditions of the problem.

Hume argued that conclusions arrived at by induction cannot be justified by any of the methods of justification common in the mathematical sciences, since inductive conclusions are, unlike those drawn from mathematical argument, at best highly probable, never certain. He argued further that such conclusions cannot be justified by appealing to what we have found in past experience, since any appeal to experience would involve an inference from the past to the future and would *ipso facto* beg the very question at issue. Hume sought some other way to justify induction but could find none. Consequently, he left the problem in this form. Since Hume's work, many philosophers tried without success to discover a justification of induction which would escape Hume's skeptical arguments, and others attempted with equal lack of success to prove that the task of justifying induction is, as Hume strongly suspected, an impossible one. Numerous arguments were offered on each side of the issue, but pitifully few turned out to be substantive, and none proved conclusive. From Kant, who was the first philosopher to consider the problem seriously, to Reichenbach, who, with the possible exception of Peirce, was the first to make a substantive contribution to it, many of the most influential philosophers in modern philosophy—Russell, Wittgenstein, Keynes, Ramsey—have grappled with the problem. But the problem has remained as much a riddle as Hume left it.

Reichenbach argued that Hume's skepticism is neither the last word on the subject nor mere Pyrrhonism. He argued that Hume's arguments, though they do not preclude a justification of induction, do succeed in establishing that induction cannot be justified by being subsumed under other independently acceptable principles. But Reichenbach pointed out that this is not the only way to justify a principle. Often, he argued, we justify a principle by showing that a policy of action in accord with it is the best means of achieving a desired end. Since Hume's argument leaves open the option of such an ends-means justification, Reichenbach concluded that it is, by itself, insufficient to warrant the conclusion that induction cannot be justified.

Reichenbach himself proposed a justification which claimed that acting in accord with the policy of making inductive predictions is the best way of coming to true conclusions about nature. Predictions which are inductively extrapolated from past experience, he argued, constitute the best wagers we can make upon future contingency. Moreover, he was able to establish that, if truths about the world can be known, we will know them by induction—at least in the long run. This feature of Reichenbach's argument came as a revelation: he had succeeded in showing *deductively* that no means of making predictions could be successful if every sort of induction were sure to fail! But even this much was too little to justify induction, since it established only a necessary condition for preferring induction to other predictive techniques. Reichenbach was thus forced to supplement this argument with others to obtain a pragmatic argument which, if sound, would provide a sufficient condition for preferring induction. Reichenbach's pragmatic argument has by no means met with unanimous acceptance among philosophers, though it has won many strong supporters.

In the course of this book we examine Reichenbach's argument in great detail and show why it is inconclusive. But, since this inconclusiveness might be only a feature of the way Reichenbach handles the argument and since there might be either another formulation of it or another argument which does what Reichenbach's fails to do, in order to provide a final solution to the problem of induction, it is necessary to demonstrate that no argument can succeed where Reichenbach's fails. To do this, we have adopted the following plan.

In the first chapter of this book we present the problem of induction and consider the claim some philosophers make that the problem is not a genuine one. Here it is shown that the problem cannot be so dismissed. The first chapter also tries to place the problem of induction in its proper position in the study of scientific methodology. The second chapter explores the concept of 'justification' in order to clarify the structure of justificatory arguments and in order to delineate the alternatives open to those seeking a justification of induction and to those seeking to rule out such a justification. The third chapter offers a reduction of the general problem of induction to a special case, success in which is shown to constitute a necessary condition for the existence of a justification of induction in the general case. This special case is the ends-means argument first suggested by Reichenbach. Here Reichenbach's argument is analyzed in detail, and the inconclusiveness found in it becomes the crux of the special case of the problem. The fourth chapter then presents a proof that it is, in principle, impossible to give a positive solution to this special case, and in this way it is shown why induction cannot be justified. What is shown is not only that Reichenbach's argument is inconclusive as it stands but that there can be no extension of it which leads to a satisfactory argument justifying induction. The final chapter first considers certain objections that might be raised to our negative solution to the problem and gives answers to each. It then considers the philosophical implications of this negative solution. It examines the doctrine of skepticism and analyzes the contention that unmitigated conventionalism concerning empirical knowledge (i.e., the view that, if there can be no justification of induction, no distinction between valid and invalid standards of evidence is possible) is an inescapable consequence of a negative solution to the problem. Here it is shown that this consequence is by no means inescapable.

Although the present book concerns a specific problem and offers a specific solution, it touches along the way upon other problems and issues in philosophy. Some receive nothing like the treatment they really deserve, while others are treated in much detail. The principle I have used is: "To each according to its relevance."

The writing of this book was greatly facilitated by several persons, and it is a pleasure to express my gratitude to them. I owe a large debt of gratitude to Professor C. G. Hempel, whose critical comments and helpful suggestions were important sources of stimulation during the early stages of my research. I am especially grateful to him for the generous giving of his time and the kindness he showed me. I wish to thank Professors Hilary Putnam and Ledger Wood for their aid and encouragement. I wish also to thank Professor Wesley Salmon for his interest and the enjoyable discussions we had about the problem of induction. I want to express my thanks to James Munz, Rod Otto, and Steven Spielman, who gave me the benefit of their criticism on various portions of the manuscript; to Samuel J. Keyser for his concern with an earlier version of the manuscript; and to Dr. Jerry A. Fodor, who helped me get the final version ready for publication and who contributed significantly to the clarification of many of its ideas. My thanks go also to Mrs. Donna Gunderson both for a fine job of typing of a previous draft and for the effort she made to accomplish a difficult piece of cryptanalysis. Finally, I wish to express my gratitude to my wife, Sylvia, for her forbearance and fortitude.

Contents

CHAPTER ONE

Why Guess at the Riddle?

1.1. Scientists seldom try to articulate the structure of their methodological principles, and, when they do, they are not often explicit in
what they say. But scientists need not be. They use these principles
in a form suitable to their needs, and these needs are rarely, though
by no means always, such as to require more than methodological
know-how. In choosing between alternative hypotheses and theories,
the scientist practices a skill acquired in his training, one whose satisfactory performance, like the exercise of all complex skills, proceeds
best when unencumbered by the further burden of discovering its
own principles of operation. This is not to say that the scientist and
the methodologist of science are *never* one and the same person. Re-
flective scientists are, in fact, in the best position to reflect upon
questions of methodology. Moreover, such reflection has produced
some of the major results both in science and in the philosophy of
science.

But the ways of disciplines diverge. Even the scientist when he
concerns himself with the philosophy of science seeks to make explicit what the practicing scientist ignores legitimately and as a
matter of course—the principles in accord with which scientific work
is done.

The philosopher of science is engaged in the task of analyzing the
logical structure of scientific concepts in order to provide an answer
to the following three questions:

(1) What methodological principles are employed in science?
(2) What is the justification for each of these principles?
(3) What considerations guide choices among hypotheses and theories when
    such principles conflict?

A full answer to (1) would consist in an exact characterization of
the principles which underlie scientific practice; that is, a clear artic-

ulation of the regularities found in the evidence-sifting, theory-constructing, and theory-evaluating behavior of scientists. An answer to (2) would consist in a satisfactory explanation of why these principles, and not others, are utilized, and, of course, when an accepted methodological principle does not admit of justification, an explanation of *why* no justification is possible. Question (2) is important not only because its answer in each particular case tells why we should draw conclusions in accord with the principle but also because an answer to it is a precondition of answering (3). For, when two methodological principles conflict or when methodological principles line up on either side of an issue, it is impossible to understand how the scientist chooses unless something is known about the justification for the principles involved. Scientists sometimes go by "hunches." Sometimes they appeal to cherished conceptions of "true science." Sometimes they simply guess and wait for the outcome of further experiments. But a philosopher of science would neglect a significant aspect of philosophy of science were he not to try to systematically formulate the rationale for such choices. If he, too, eschews reconstructing the scheme for making such decisions in a systematic and rational way and instead plays a hunch, guesses or speculates, he is seriously remiss. But this reconstruction presupposes an exact knowledge of the justifications of each of the principles which may enter into such conflicts, since this reconstruction must proceed by placing restrictions on the use of principles, thus limiting their application relative to the employment of other principles with which they may compete.

In this sense answering (2) opens the possibility of answering (3). An answer to (3) would consist in criteria for assessing the relative merits of the justificatory bases of conflicting methodological principles in terms of the features of various types of conflict situations. Even a partial answer to (3) in terms of such criteria would provide an explanation for certain cases where scientists choose a hypothesis or theory which is favored by some methodological principles over one which is favored by other, apparently equally cogent, principles.

Let us consider an example. A complete answer to (1) would certainly include the principle known as "Ockham's razor." This methodological canon cautions against positing entities in excess of those necessary to the explanations a theory affords. The justification of the principle is that excessive proliferation of entities proportionately weakens the evidential support which provides the theory's empirical

2

substantiation. Roughly speaking, given a body of evidence, that hypothesis or theory is, *ceteris paribus*, supported best that requires the evidence to support least conceptual weight. The more excess weight a theory gains, the stronger its ontological claims, the weaker and more hazardous it becomes as an extrapolation from the evidence of past experience. This justification shows that the ground upon which inferences in conformity with Ockham's razor are drawn are simply those upon which ordinary inductive inferences are based. Thus this justification reveals why we should draw inferences in conformity with Ockham's razor, because it shows what the reasons are for preferring this principle to other principles of the *same type*, that is, alternative principles which would condone various forms of proliferation. But it also begins to answer question (3). For now we know something about what considerations will be relevant should Ockham's razor conflict with other principles. Such justifications give us a point of comparison for methodological principles of *different types*, so that we may appraise them relative to one another and establish a policy for conflict situations.

Perhaps we may some day be able to say something definite regarding the abilities of skilled scientists to make judgments in cases where their methodological guides conflict. Today, however, this is hardly feasible. The more modest program is, therefore, to concentrate on questions (1) and (2). The pressing problems are thus those of explication and justification.

The problem of induction is clearly an instance of question (2).[1] It arises because the choice of a hypothesis must of necessity be made in advance of any knowledge of the indefinitely many events about which the hypothesis has something to say. Hypotheses are generalizations. They say of anything that has a certain property P_1 that it also has a certain other property P_2. They cover all things to which the property P_1 applies, and so they cover not only those which we have observed to possess P_2 but an unlimited number of unexamined things as well. A hypothesis that fails to conform to the known facts is simply false, but a statement that fails to assert something beyond them is not a hypothesis at all but merely a report of past experience. With hypotheses, then, there is an omnipresent gap between what we know and what we claim. It is this gap that makes

---

[1] This is not meant to imply that there is no problem of explicating the rules of inductive inference. There are, in fact, many problems which are still at the level of question (1). For example, see Goodman (13), pp. 63–120.

inductive leaps necessary. For only by bridging such gaps do we go beyond experience to learn something new about the world. The principle which allows us to bridge the gap is the principle of induction. In an inductive inference we argue that, since all cases of P_1 in the past have been cases of P_2, we may conclude that all future cases of P_1 will likewise be cases of P_2. The problem of induction is the question of how we know that such inferences are trustworthy; how we know our bridges may not begin collapsing some day? The problem is to justify the principle behind our inferences from the past behavior of things to their future behavior.

There is one compelling reason for taking the problem of induction seriously, but, curiously enough, it is never cited to support the legitimacy of the problem. It is this: The problem of induction is of fundamental importance for the philosophy of science because the solution to numerous other problems in this field depends upon some disposition of it. In the first place, a full answer to (3) clearly presupposes a final disposition of the problem of induction. But, besides, the fact that the principle of induction is a ubiquitous feature of scientific choice means that even a partial answer to (3) demands its disposition. Second, an answer to (2) requires such a disposition in cases where a methodological principle derives its justification entirely from the principle of induction.

1.2. As we indicated above, the problem of induction is not a scientific problem but one which arises when we reflect on science. The same is true of the relationship of this problem to daily life. Ordinary people and scientists alike take factual conclusions to be adequately established if they are warranted by the available evidence, warrantedness being, in general, determined by conformity to inductive standards. Of course, the process of acquiring empirical knowledge does not always run smoothly. Often inductive predictions and generalizations are contravened by further experience; but, as a matter of actual practice, such cases never cause us seriously to question the adequacy of induction. To the scientist and the citizen the universe manifests uniformities, and induction is taken for granted as one feature of the method by which they are revealed. Although using induction as a scientific tool may sometimes become a difficult and complicated matter, no philosophical problem exists at this level. Science and daily life proceed according to the results of induction, and it remains a tool whose employment is always accepted.

Philosophers, however, are wont to be skeptical of presuppositions.

4

So it is not surprising that a philosopher has raised doubts concerning the acceptance of induction. Aristotle was the first to observe that the difference between a formal argument and an inductive argument is a matter of the latter's non-demonstrativeness. But it remained for the great eighteenth-century philosopher David Hume to grasp the significance of this observation and to base upon it a doctrine denying any epistemological sanction for the confidence we normally place in inductive inferences.

The crux of Aristotle's observation is that, because what has occurred in the past does not logically restrict what may occur in the future, arguments leading to conclusions about unknown cases must be non-demonstrative and as such logically inconclusive. But, questioned Hume, if such arguments are logically inconclusive, how can they provide reliable information? Let us modernize this point somewhat. Inductive conclusions, since they tell us something about unobserved cases, are neither summaries of past experience nor analytic consequences of such summaries. If they were derived deductively from statements about what has been observed, they could assure us only of something of which our premises already assure us, and, thus, they could tell us only something we already "know." Without inductive inference or some other form of non-demonstrative inference, our knowledge of the world would be confined to what we could directly observe. But because such inferences produce conclusions pertaining to cases not included in what has been observed, and so extend knowledge beyond the directly observable, inductive arguments cannot be justified on deductive grounds.

But, according to Hume, they cannot be justified on the grounds of experience either. We make one prediction rather than another because we inductively extrapolate past uniformities. How, asks Hume, do we determine that the policy of choosing predictions which conform to inductive projections from observed uniformities is a reliable one? We are tempted to say that we judge the reliability of this policy by looking at the record. But, as Hume points out, this option is not open, because we cannot legitimately justify the general policy of appealing to experience by appealing to experience. Since it is this very type of appeal to the record whose justifiability is in question, justificatory arguments based on what has been experienced merely go in a circle and beg the very question at issue.

Let us modernize again. If we express the inductive policy in the form of a rule for framing predictions about unknown events, we obtain the following: Generalize the regularity found in events so far observed and posit this as the regularity governing all events of the same kind. We may now ask Hume's question by inquiring what justification there is for accepting this rule as a reliable way to obtain predictions. Such a justification might take either of the two following forms: (i) a factual contention that in the past regularities discovered in experience have endured in the future (we know that nature is such as to guarantee the success of this rule) or (ii) a contention that in the past this rule has afforded a convincing record of highly reliable predictions about the future (we know that the rule is such as to guarantee success with nature). Now Hume's criticism can be put in the form of a claim that both (i) and (ii) themselves rely on this rule. Form (i) relies on the rule to conclude from the fact that, if past regularities have continued into the future, future regularities will do so too. Form (ii) relies on the rule to conclude from the fact that, if the rule has been successful in the past, it will also be successful in the future. Here the rule is assumed in order to project the past association between the use of the rule and success in prediction. Hence both (i) and (ii) employ the very rule whose reliability they are meant to justify. Thus both are viciously circular, for their conclusions can be acceptable only if what they assert is acceptable to begin with.

This argument of Hume's has proved thoroughly unpalatable to many philosophers, not because it has been found to contain a fallacy, but, rather one might say, because it has not been found to contain one. On the other hand, there are many philosophers who accept it as it stands. Again, some philosophers, though impressed, find it insufficiently convincing to dissuade them from continuing to look for a justification of induction. Others are strongly inclined to Humean skepticism because it is polemically the most comfortable position. A good number ignore the problem, and, finally, an equally good number reject it as unreal.

None of these philosophical positions will appear obviously correct upon one's first encounter with the problem of induction. Rather, one's initial reaction to Hume's skeptical arguments is likely to be simple puzzlement. On the one hand, one is unwilling to believe that these arguments conclusively prove that induction cannot be justified, perhaps because one is psychologically unable to accept this conclusion or perhaps because one is not yet convinced that there is no way to avoid Hume's arguments. On the other hand, one cannot but be struck by their cogency and by how refractory they are to logical criticism. A re-examination of the problem of induction which hopes to arrive at the truth proceeds best when it proceeds from such puzzlement.

The legitimacy of the problem of induction is sometimes questioned because it is not a practical problem. It is true that this problem appears to have no practical import. The unreserved trust we place in inductive inference will not be undermined however the problem is resolved. Hume himself said, "Nature will always maintain her rights and prevail in the end over any abstract reasoning whatsoever."[2] But, though we may fully agree with Hume, this is no reason for questioning the legitimacy of the problem. All theoretical investigations share, to some extent, this sort of impracticality. Pure mathematics does not aim at solving practical problems, and its systems are only incidentally models for the special sciences. The usefulness of the results of pure mathematics has nothing to do with their applications in empirical science as far as the pure mathematician is concerned—no more so than the theoretical physicist's abstract constructions are for him justified by the thermonuclear weapons they lead to. Moreover, it is always possible that something of practical significance may come from a purely theoretical inquiry, and this is a possibility that cannot be prejudged.

The attitude we are taking can be summarized as follows: The problem is to determine whether induction can be justified philosophically. We wish to know whether we can devise a rationale for extrapolating observed regularities to similar cases which have not yet been observed. Our motivation for seeking an answer does not come from a belief that things would be somehow better if we could find a justification. We wish merely to know whether philosophy can offer a basis for believing that inductive predictions and generalizations are reliable. If we can discover such a justification, we wish to know this and also what sort of justification it is. If not, we wish to know this, too; and we should like to know exactly why not.

1.3. Stating the problem of induction in precise terms is not easy. For one thing, certain difficulties arise which can be adequately treated only after considerable progress has been made toward the disposition of the problem. Nonetheless, without going as far as an exact specification, we can now formulate a reasonably precise version

2 Hume (18), p. 55.

of the problem and indicate the sort of difficulties that stand in the way of further precision.

Induction is a species of non-demonstrative inference, though it is by no means the only such species. By "non-demonstrative inference" we understand the forming of a conclusion regarding all instances of a certain class from a knowledge of some proper subset consisting of its known instances. As Hume's arguments show, such conclusions are never logical consequences of their premises, though these premises usually confirm them or make them more probable. But there is a wide variety of different rules for drawing non-demonstrative conclusions from the same matters of fact, and non-inductive examples are as easy to find as ways of systematically violating the rule of induction. Since induction projects the regularity exhibited by the known instances of a phenomenon to every instance of this phenomenon, all that is necessary to construct one of the indefinitely many non-inductive rules of non-demonstrative inference is to select a specific type of departure from the inductive projection and form a rule to project it. And this can be done in a systematic way so that we get the same type of departure regardless of what the inductive projection may be. One such rule we may call the "don't-believe-what-you-see rule." This rule instructs us to project the very opposite of an inductive projection; it is as though the unknown events in a population bear the least possible resemblance to the observed events. Thus, according to this rule, if we observe a great many spinsters each of whom peeks under her bed before retiring, we are instructed to predict that no spinster will do this in the future. Perhaps, according to another non-inductive rule, we are instructed to predict that only a few spinsters will peek; while, according to yet another, we are instructed to predict that very many, though not all, will perform this ritual.

These considerations lead us to a new formulation of the problem of induction. Does there exist a way to justify choosing the inductive rule from among all the rules of non-demonstrative inference? Can we show that the choice of the inductive rule is a better choice than the choice of any non-inductive non-demonstrative rule? Is it possible, in a non-circular way, to say why the inductive rule is preferable to, for example, the don't-believe-what-you-see rule as a means of making reliable predictions?

This is certainly a clear statement of the problem, but it is still not clear enough. To obtain a better formulation, however, it is necessary to characterize more precisely both the inductive rule and the non-inductive rules. One very natural approach along this line is to say that induction posits the persistence of *regularities,* while a non-inductive rule posits a type of *irregularity,* and to concentrate on explicating the difference between regularities and irregularities. In fact, for practical purposes we can even do without an explication of the concept of a regularity. Each of us can recognize a regularity when he sees one. We no more need such an explication than we need a syntactical definition of the concept of grammaticality to enable us to recognize a grammatical utterance. Nevertheless, without such an explication an approach to the problem via the concept of a regularity is theoretically unacceptable.

Clearly, this approach does not permit us to begin with a general characterization of induction and work back to an explication of the concept of a regularity. Rather, it demands a characterization of the concept 'regularity' which is independent of induction; otherwise this approach would circle back on itself without offering clarification. But this we do not have. This approach founders because it fails to take account of the fact that by 'regularity' we mean 'something which occurs in conformity to a rule'. This implies that by a regularity in a series of events a pattern which conforms to the rule of induction is meant, whereas by an irregularity a pattern which does not conform is meant.

The fact of the matter is simply that the concepts 'regularity' and 'inductive rule' are essentially the same. The immediately preceding considerations show that the concept of a regularity involves the notion of an inductive rule, and it is easy to show, conversely, that the concept of an inductive rule involves the notion of a regularity. An examination of the form of an inductive rule reveals that such a rule takes the form of an instruction to posit the persistence of an observed regularity. Clearly, if a rule is to be inductive instead of counterinductive, it must project regularities from known events instead of irregularities. To do this, the formulation of the rule will have to contain the characterizing features of a regularity: An inductive rule will be of the form, 'If something is true of all the known members of a class and it satisfies such-and-such conditions, posit that it is a regularity governing the unknown members also'. Since 'such-and-such conditions' are the characterizing features of a regularity, we cannot characterize induction without explicating the concept of a regularity. Thus these concepts are, at bottom, the same.

Let us try a more direct approach. Typical of the regularities which induction assures us will persist and on which we continually rely are the following: the rising and setting of the sun each day; the ebb and flow of the tide each lunar day; the moon's repetition of its phase cycle each month; and the constancy of the average radiation of the sun each year. If we are asked why we believe these patterns will remain unchanged, we would probably reply simply, "Because they have always done so." We might mention theoretical reasons by invoking Newtonian mechanics or some other physical theory. But, if the point were pressed, we would ultimately fall back on our belief that the empirical generalizations which comprise the theory's confirmation basis will remain intact. In this sense, then, every empirical argument, even quite complicated and abstract theoretical ones, involves a reliance on the persistence of certain regularities. So the reply, "Because they have always done so," stands alone.

But this reply is tantamount to saying that these patterns are regularities. What, then, is it about them that leads us to this identification? If asked this, we would probably reply in something like the following way: "They represent a uniform succession of co-occurring events. Whenever we find the first of two events always accompanied by the occurrence of the second, such a sequence of events exhibits a regularity."

This answer is a fairly sound rule of thumb, but it is not yet an adequate explication of the notion of a regularity. One may argue that this characterization is too narrow on the grounds that some patterns of events we would like to call "regularities" are not actually exceptionless. Scientists, it may be added, are sometimes forced to tolerate such cases. This objection, however, is not an important one and can be answered by the counterargument that scientists are no happier with incompatible statements than anyone else. They seek to resolve such paradoxes either by dropping the exception as an error of observation or by explaining it with an interpretation on which it is not a counterexample or by revising the generality so as to accommodate it. But, be this as it may, clearly such cases would be quite insignificant were we to have an otherwise adequate characterization of a regularity.

The crucial difficulty is that this reply offers a characterization that is too wide, for it allows as regularities patterns which no one would ever construe as such. Let us start with an example. Smith asserts that gold dissolves in aqua regia; that is, that the events of immersing a sample of gold in a mixture of nitric and hydrochloric acids and its subsequent dissolution form a true regularity. To support his claim, Smith offers a great many cases in which gold has dissolved in aqua regia and evidence to the effect that no case where gold has failed to dissolve exists. By the previous characterization of a regularity we are led to conclude that this is indeed a regularity. But this is not all by any means. For, given this characterization of a regularity, there is a general method for producing an indefinitely large number of 'regularities' each of which affords different predictions in many cases.[3] It works like this: We introduce a new predicate 'transolves' defined so as to apply to anything which is placed in aqua regia before the time Smith finished gathering evidence and which dissolves but to anything else only if immersion in aqua regia transmutes it to lead. The hypothesis that gold transolves expresses a regularity according to the above characterization of that notion. For, whenever we observed a sample of gold in aqua regia, either it was immersed before we terminated collecting evidence and was dissolved or it was immersed later and transmutes to lead. So every item in our evidence is as much an instance of this 'regularity' as it is an instance of the more natural one. Moreover, it is quite clear that the list of such 'regularities' can be extended to any length whatever merely by constructing new predicates in a similar fashion (i.e., by employing effects other than transmutation to lead). Since any body of evidence from which we may wish to generalize can be shown in this way to exhibit any bizarre regularity, this characterization of the notion of a regularity must be counted too wide. Consequently, we must find a way to limit the class of 'regularities' countenanced by our characterization to just those we would ordinarily license as genuine regularities.

What has gone wrong is simply that we have failed to take account of one of the primary factors in scientific choice—simplicity. Taking simplicity into account, there is an obvious and natural way of so limiting the characterization. Thus we achieve a characterization of a regularity as the simplest uniform succession of co-occurring events and consequently obtain an inductive rule which is very like that proposed by Wittgenstein in the *Tractatus:* "The process of induction is the process of assuming the *simplest* law that can be made to harmonize with our experience."[4] For every pair of events which can be defined over a sample and which always occur concomitantly,

---

[3] This difficulty will receive more extensive treatment in sec. 4.4 (chap. iv). The origin of this problem is to be found in Goodman (13), pp. 73–80.

[4] Wittgenstein (39), p. 180.

there is one pair which is the simplest co-occurrence, and this co-occurrence our new characterization takes as the regularity in the sample. Induction is then the rule which instructs us to posit the persistence of the regularities in samples.

By introducing the notion of simplicity, we attain a more adequate formulation but still not one which is precise enough. For now we are left with "simplicity" as an unexplicated term. It will be recalled that we began this discussion by saying that the main source of trouble in stating the problem rigorously is that difficulties arise which can be overcome only after considerable progress toward a disposition is made. Explicating the concept of simplicity which is relevant here is such a difficulty. However, we can provide a general characterization of simplicity which will serve our purposes until we require something better.

Intuitively, the notion of simplicity is simple; but, once we inquire into its exact structure, we are beset by a multitude of complexities. What we shall try to do here is to separate the various senses of simplicity and determine which of them is appropriate to the problem of induction.

First of all, there is a sense of simplicity in which it means familiarity. In this sense, for most people classical physics is simpler than relativity, psychoanalysis simpler than Hullian learning theory, and geocentric astronomy is simpler than heliocentric astronomy. But this conception cannot be the one we seek, because it cannot serve as an adequate basis for choosing between regularities and irregularities—between hypotheses each of which conforms to the available evidence but differs for predictions beyond it. For simplicity thus construed would discriminate against new or less familiar hypotheses. Moreover, since human beings display marked individual differences in regard to what they find familiar, familiarity could provide no truly objective standard of simplicity. Thus simplicity construed as familiarity would make science both too reactionary and too subjective. Hence what we wish to understand by simplicity is not to be confused with familiarity.

For exactly the same reasons no other psychological sense of the term will do. Often we use the term "simple" in the sense of "easy of comprehension," and sometimes we use it in the sense of "natural." But neither of these senses would afford a reasonable guide for choosing between hypotheses because they, too, would tend to make science overly conservative and subjective.

Another sense of simplicity is what we may call "notational simplicity." This is the sort of simplicity which makes one system of notation better than another because it is easier to handle or exhibits the structure of what it describes more perspicuously. Examples of this type of simplicity are the metric system versus the system of yards and inches, and a propositional calculus containing implication, negation, conjunction, disjunction, and equivalence versus one with only Sheffer's stroke. But this is not the sort of simplicity we require because it relates only to logically equivalent constructions, whereas any choice among competitive hypotheses is a choice between logically incompatible constructions.

Still another type of simplicity which should be considered may be referred to as "economy of fundamental concepts." This is the sort of simplicity we strive for when we try to reduce the fundamental concepts of a system to the barest minimum without, at the same time, reducing the consequence set of the system. A system which is simple in this sense gives us a deep insight into what ideas actually underlie it. But simplicity of this kind is not appropriate for our purpose because, in terms of it, only axiomatic systems can be compared and, at that, only such systems whose consequence sets are equivalent or related by proper inclusion.

From the previous considerations it is evident that the conception of simplicity we want relates to what empirical hypotheses assert about the world. It relates to the properties and relations which characterize particular entities, their behavior, systems, and processes. Newton's famous dictum, "Nature is pleased with simplicity, and effects not the pomp of superfluous causes,"[5] refers to this kind of simplicity, and so does Galileo's remark, "When, therefore, I observe a stone initially at rest falling from a considerable height and gradually acquiring new increments of speed, why should I not believe that such increments come about in the simplest, the most plausible way?"[6] This notion of simplicity is intended by such remarks as: "A linear function of a variable is a simpler hypothesis than a quadratic"; "A watch is simpler than the human brain"; "The behavior of an amoeba is simpler than that of a primate"; "Alcohol has simpler properties than water"; etc.

Simplicity criteria are needed to enable us to choose among a batch of hypotheses each of whose verified consequences agree but some of

---

[5] Newton (24), p. 71.   [6] Galileo (11), p. 154.

whose untested consequences are incompatible with some of those of the others. Some simplicity criteria are readily at hand. Given that one of two hypotheses posits fewer entities or causes, or requires fewer concepts (properties or relations) to be formulated, so long as there is no difference in the structural complexity of the entities or causes or concepts, this hypothesis is simpler, and hence its predictions about unknown events should be accepted. And, conversely, given a parity in the number of entities, causes, or concepts, the simpler hypothesis is the one positing the least complicated entities or causes or employing the least complicated concepts. But, beyond such crude criteria as these, an immense job of explication is called for in order to construct simplicity criteria which will make all the decisions that have to be made and make them in an acceptable way.

Some of the problems that lie ahead are these. First, such notions as 'complicated' and 'more complicated', as applying to entities, causes, and concepts, will have to be analyzed. In comparing hypotheses in order to make actual decisions about which is simpler, the counting of entities, causes, and concepts may be regarded as trivial, but measuring complication may not. And it is immediately evident that, if this analysis is to be successful, we shall have to provide a successful analysis of such concepts as 'entity', 'cause', and 'concept'. Second, such criteria will have to specify what to do in cases where one hypothesis invokes a complicated entity while its competitor employs a simpler entity but uses considerably more complicated concepts to formulate its behavior. There are a multitude of variations on this theme; worse yet, besides conflicts where each hypothesis is simpler in one sense and more complex in another, we shall have to take into account the relative effect of other methodological considerations when they become involved in conflicts already involving simplicity.

Thus the task of explicating this notion of simplicity is a tremendously difficult one. Fortunately, however, each problem in philosophy can be dealt with without investigating every problem at once. We will have to say considerably more about the explication of simplicity and consider some of the work of philosophers who have contributed to such an explication, but the full story is not necessary here. In fact, most of what we need to say concerns the logical form and justification of simplicity criteria rather than the exact character of the explicatum. We shall return to this matter.

1.4. A few words should be said by way of clarifying a matter which usually comes up in connection with discussions of induction.

This is the question of the scope and limits of inductive inference in empirical science.

It is clear to anyone who has examined modern empirical science that to concern one's self exclusively with induction is to neglect some of the most powerful techniques scientists use and some of the most characteristic features of theoretical science. Some philosophers argue from this fact that the problem of induction should not be an object of serious concern in the philosophical analysis of empirical science. They claim that induction is unimportant in the scheme of things in science when compared to other patterns of inference. But one thing overlooked by those who argue in this way is that, though induction may be in some respects a less powerful scientific tool than others and may be less characteristic of theoretical science than others, a serious concern with questions about induction may be a necessary step in coming to understand these other tools. And it seems quite unlikely that we can answer questions of types (2) and (3) about such tools without considering the same questions in the case of induction.

A philosophical issue has even grown up around this point. The issue is whether or not induction, together with suitable definitions and theorems of the calculus of probability, is sufficient to handle all scientific inferences except those of a purely deductive character. This issue has occasioned many interesting arguments both pro and con, and each side has enlisted the support of influential philosophers. Some philosophers, notably Reichenbach, have argued that induction by simple enumeration with the mathematical theory of probability is adequate to reconstruct all scientific inference.[7] Others, of course, have claimed that there are equally important inference patterns which go far beyond the scope of induction. It is customary for the latter side to cite instances of what Duhem has called "hypothetical explanation" as evidence for their view. An example of this pattern is Chadwick's inference to the existence of neutrons: When beryllium is bombarded by fast alpha particles, particles are emitted from the nuclei which have far greater penetrating power than the alpha particles themselves. If these particles were uncharged and of a mass about equal to that of a proton, their immense penetrating power would be explained by their failure to cause ionization when passing through gas and their refractoriness to deflection by an electrical field. Hence, neutrons exist.

However, this issue is irrelevant here. If Reichenbach's side is cor-

[7] Reichenbach (32), pp. 429–44.

rect, then, since in the last analysis every scientific inference is inductive, the criticism that the problem of induction is not of serious concern is wrong. On the other hand, if the other side happens to be correct, and there are patterns of inference which are not reducible to induction, this criticism is still wrong. Consider the Chadwick example again. The argument is sound only if materials such as beryllium, boron, and lithium invariably emit particles of immense penetrating power when bombarded by fast alpha particles. Had Chadwick not inferred the persistence of this regularity from the results of his own experiments and those of Bothe and Becker and Curie and Joliot, he could not have given his hypothetical explanation. This explanation thus presupposes an inductive inference. Whatever else may be involved in establishing this momentous conclusion, induction certainly is. Moreover, the scientists who, since Chadwick, have extended our knowledge of the structure of the nucleus continue to rely on the persistence of this regularity. Hence we may say that the scope of induction is as wide as that of scientific inference itself, though probably scientific inference employs deeper patterns of explanation than induction. The criticism is, therefore, belied by the range of application induction has in science and may be bypassed.

1.5. Historically, philosophers have taken one of two positions on the problem of induction. The skeptics, following Hume, deny that a justification of induction is possible. They claim that the conditions of the problem demand the impossible and so prohibit any solution. The inductivists, as we shall call them, maintain that no such thing has been shown and that a positive solution can be found. Neither position, it must be admitted, is a homogeneous one, but both have enlisted the support of important modern philosophers.

Bertrand Russell indorsed the inductivist viewpoint when he wrote:

I am convinced that induction must have validity of some kind in some degree, but the problem of showing how and why it is valid remains unsolved. . . . Until it is solved, the rational man will doubt whether his food will nourish him, and whether the sun will rise tomorrow.[8]

F. P. Ramsey, speaking for the opposition, has written:

It is true that if anyone has not the habit of induction, we cannot prove to him that he is wrong; but there is nothing peculiar in that. If a man doubts his memory or his perception we cannot prove to him that they

---

[8] Russell (33), p. 14.

are trustworthy; to ask for such a thing to be proved its to cry for the moon, and the same is true of induction.[9]

A. N. Whitehead once referred to the problem of induction as "the despair of philosophy,"[10] and C. D. Broad called it "the scandal of philosophy."[11] Clearly, both Whitehead and Broad were firm inductivists. But Ramsey replies for the skeptic's position when he says:

Since the time of Hume a great deal has been written about the justification of inductive inference. Hume showed that it could not be reduced to deductive inference or justified by formal logic. So far as it goes his demonstration seems to me final; and the suggestion of Mr. Keynes that it can be got round by regarding induction as a form of probable inference cannot in my view be maintained. But to suppose that the situation which results from this is a scandal to philosophy is, I think, a mistake[12]

And supporting the inductivist position is no less a philosopher than the eminent American pragmatist C. S. Peirce, who writes:

I undertake to demonstrate mathematically that the validity of induction, in the proper sense of the term, that is to say, experimental reasoning, follows, through the lemmas of probabilities, from the rudiments of the doctrine of necessary consequences, without any assumption whatever about the future being like the past, or the uniformity of nature, or any such vague principle. I shall set forth the reasoning in strict accuracy of form; and I defy anybody to find a flaw in it.[13]

Wittgenstein's remark on the possibility of justifying inductive inference is such as might stand at the conclusion of Hume's own argument: "This process, however, has no logical foundation but only a psychological one. It is clear that there are no grounds for believing that the simplest course of events will really happen."[14]

These quotations serve as a vignette depicting the two opposed philosophical traditions stemming from Hume's work. But, as can readily be seen from some of them, these traditions have mingled with others, thereby linking the problem of induction to other issues. No problem is an island unto itself.

Both skeptics and inductivists are very much aware that the problem of induction is intimately bound up with the task of locating an exact boundary between methods of inquiry which produce genuine

[9] Ramsey (29), p. 197.

[10] Whitehead (38), p. 34.

[11] Broad (4), p. 67.

[12] Ramsey (29), pp. 196–97.

[13] Peirce (25), II, 58.

[14] Wittgenstein (39), p. 180.

knowledge and those which issue in unsubstantial substitutes. Both recognize that to provide such a distinction is an extremely important job for philosophy. The inductivist, as the quotation from Russell illustrates, believes that a justification of induction is a *sine qua non* of any such separation of methods. The skeptic, as Ramsey's remarks indicate, believes that the attempt to differentiate valid from spurious modes of establishing beliefs is neither thwarted nor even hampered by abandoning the search for a justification. For, contrary to the inductivist, for the skeptic these are two entirely independent questions, one of which is a pseudo-question. In the opinion of the skeptic, connecting the problem of induction to the problem of distinguishing real and spurious knowledge works to the disadvantage of the latter program by putting unnecessary obstacles in the path of its completion. This is what motivates his desire to have done with the problem of induction once and for all. The inductivist, on the other hand, is motivated by the fear that, if induction cannot be justified, empirical knowledge is, at bottom, purely a matter of arbitrary convention. What is believed is believed because it is established by a certain method which compels its acceptance. If there is no better justification for one method than for another, there is no better reason for one belief than for another. Thus we might as well believe what we wish, though we must accept whatever others choose to believe in a spirit of complete tolerance.

Some skeptics would be inclined to reply as follows: The question whether induction can be justified makes no difference to establishing a demarcation line between valid and invalid methods because we have a simple rule which suffices in all cases where a knowledge claim turns on fact. The rule is that conformity with induction establishes the soundness of a non-demonstrative inference, while violation of this canon establishes the unsoundness of such an inference. There is no reason why the desired epistemological distinction cannot be drawn by this rule. There is, of course, a task of refinement remaining, since the degree to which the method of induction is refined is the degree of precision with which the line can be drawn. But this is another story.

This, however, is an unfortunate reply because the problem is not whether a line can be drawn by *some* rule but rather that there are too many rules and too many lines. Thus the inductivist can easily reply that this rejoinder comes down to the same horrifying consequence; we might as well draw one line as another, but we must tolerantly accept someone else's demarcation regardless of where it is drawn.

Does the impossibility of justifying induction preclude the possibility of distinguishing between trustworthy and untrustworthy methods of fixing belief? We will return to this question after we have finished with the problem of induction. If induction can be justified, the question need not bother us. If induction cannot be justified, perhaps a knowledge of why it cannot will help us to provide a satisfactory answer.

1.6. Skeptics sometimes grow impatient with the problem of induction. Then the prospect of trivializing the problem out of existence becomes very attractive. Many attempts to do just this have been made, and therefore it is incumbent on the present study, by way of justifying so lengthy a treatment, to show why these far more concise treatments are inadequate.

Many skeptics are content to reiterate Hume. This, however, is a sheer waste of time. Hume's polemic, as we shall show later, proves only that one form of justification is ruled out. Since Hume, Reichenbach and Peirce have established the applicability of a type of justificatory argument which escapes Hume's criticisms. Thus Humean arguments are now far less convincing than they once seemed and can by no means be taken as the final word.

Some skeptics argue that linguistic considerations show that terms such as "reasonable," "rational," etc., contain in their meaning the idea of inductive establishment, and so the question, "Why believe in induction?" can be answered simply by saying, "Because it is reasonable (or rational, etc.) to do so and unreasonable (or irrational, etc.) to do otherwise." But those who have used this argument have never shown that the meaning of these words are as they say they are. And there seems to be much room for doubt. The question is whether calling something "reasonable" or "rational" means that it is agreeable to the *appropriate* standards, whatever they may be, or whether calling something "reasonable" or "rational" means that it is agreeable to certain specific standards, induction in particular. It is thus a question of the abstractness of the meaning of these terms. The question for this linguistic argument is whether *reasonable* or *rational* means *established by reliable canons of non-demonstrative inference* or *established by inductive canons*. That these terms have the latter meaning seems dubious in light of the fact that, when specific standards are most conspicuously present, as in the case of a rigorous formal proof of a mathematical theorem, we do not say the argument is reasonable or rational but rather that it is a conclusive demonstration. Furthermore, in many cases there simply are no specific standards.

Be this as it may, even if we grant the purported meaning connection, the argument begs the question. As Salmon has put it:

> It sounds very much as if the whole argument [that reasonable beliefs are, by definition, beliefs which are inductively supported] has the function of transferring to the word "inductive" all of the honorific connotations of the word "reasonable," quite apart from whether induction is good for anything. The resulting justification of induction amounts to this: If you use inductive procedures you can call yourself "reasonable" —*and isn't that nice!*[15]

The inductivist is worried by the prospect of his someday being in the situation where he pines for the good old days when being rational meant something. To the inductivist, then, such linguistic arguments merely change the question because, assuming rationality involves inductive inference, it is rationality that is up for justification. But, actually, the question is begged, or rather just neglected, because the real issue is whether the conclusions of inductive inference can, in general, be relied on to be truthful.

Another skeptical argument that is sometimes heard maintains that seeking a justification of induction is foolish because such a justification must necessarily rest on at least one unjustifiable premiss. In substance, the argument is as follows: Any proposed justification will have the form of a deductive argument with premises and a conclusion drawn from them. As such, it must be logically sound if it is to justify anything. But a necessary condition of the logical soundness of an argument is that it conform to the principle of non-contradiction; that is, the conjunction formed by taking each of the premisses as a conjunct must be logically consistent with the conclusion. Hence a premiss of such a justificatory argument is the principle of non-contradiction itself, which, as will be granted by everyone, is completely unjustifiable. Therefore, why should we break our heads over the search for a justification of induction when, of necessity, we will be back where we started from with an unjustifiable principle even if we succeed?

That this argument possesses a sort of simple charm is undeniable,

---

[15] Salmon (35), p. 42.

but, unfortunately for the sake of our ease and convenience, it depends upon an unacceptable tacit assumption. This assumption is that all the principles on which an acceptable justificatory argument rests must themselves be justifiable. We may interpret this assumption in either of two ways. Under one interpretation, it says that *every* justification, and so in particular a justification of induction, must rest on justifiable principles only. Under the other, it says that only a justification of induction (with perhaps certain other principles which need not be considered in this context) requires its underlying principles to be justifiable. The former interpretation need not be taken seriously because, if accepted, it would make utter nonsense of the whole process of rational justification, leaving us to settle disagreements by coercion, threat, propaganda, trickery, and brute force. Thus the latter interpretation, as it were, wins by default. But interpreted in this way the assumption takes on an air of complete arbitrariness. Why the exception in some but not in other cases? It is patently impossible independently to justify non-contradiction. Thus any principles whose justifiability is made to depend on that of non-contradiction are thereby rendered unjustifiable. So, trivially, induction is rendered unjustifiable. But, since there is no reason given for thus foredooming the inductivist's enterprise, the skeptic's argument actually amounts to nothing more than a blind fiat that induction is unjustifiable. If the question is whether induction is justifiable on *acceptable* assumptions, then merely to stipulate that it is not justifiable in the absolute sense begs it, regardless of how devious a form the stipulation takes.

However, there are more systematic reasons for dismissing this argument. It is generally conceded that unjustified principles, like independent causes and abstract entities, ought not be multiplied beyond necessity. But a philosopher in trying to justify induction is trying to reduce by one the number of unjustified principles. Thus he must certainly be counted on the side of the angels. There is per se nothing wrong with harboring unjustified principles. There is no stigma in those cases where we cannot help ourselves. We become culpable when we tolerate an unjustified principle which, with some effort, could be justified.

The above skeptical polemics are only a few of those used by the impatient. It is both impossible and profitless to consider all such arguments. In the course of this book, especially at the beginning of chapter iii, we shall have reason to examine others.

1.7. What is involved in the skeptic's thesis is a demand that the inductivist should abandon his search for a justification. Thus anyone who espouses skepticism places himself in the position of asking others to cease what they are doing. Since the inquirer has a prima facie right to continue whatever program of research he may be engaged in, the skeptic thereby incurs the obligation to provide conclusive reasons for his skepticism. Anything less may persuade the skeptic to invest his own time in what he considers a more fruitful line of research, but is unworthy of some of the accomplishments of inductivists. Thus the skeptic, if he is to be responsible, must conclusively substantiate his claim that attempting to justify induction is attempting to do the impossible.

This is what I intend to do in this book. I propose to answer the inductivist in a way that is fully conclusive—one which not only offers an adequate rejoinder to existing proposals for a justification but also provides systematic reasons why induction must always remain unjustified.

The problem of induction, as so far stated, is the question of why we prefer a rule projecting the endurance of past regularities over rules projecting the endurance of past irregularities. This is not to ask why the rule we actually use to make non-demonstrative inferences is expected to lead to conclusions which hold good in future and unexamined past cases or to ask why we confidently accept it as a guide to action. For that is a psychological question whose answer need bear no resemblance to what justifies such behavior if it, in fact, has a justification. The epistemological question is: What makes it a sound policy to frame predictions and generalizations inductively and to believe that they are more reliable than those obtained by any alternative method? There may be nothing to justify our preference for inductively established conclusions, but there may be a great deal to be said by way of explaining why we persist in the inductive faith.

In latter chapters we will take up the challenge in Peirce's declaration and meet it by furnishing a conclusive solution of the problem of induction. We will make no attempt to argue that the problem is meaningless, since it is amply clear that the thesis that induction can be justified is a meaningful one. Rather, the argument we shall advance will show that the conditions of the problem prohibit any positive solution. This was the line of attack taken by Hume himself. He argued that there are only two ways to justify induction, deductively and inductively; that each committed a fallacy; and that, therefore, there is no justification of induction. As will become increasingly evident, our argument will employ Hume's line of attack, presuppose his argument, and carry his reasoning far beyond the point to which he developed it, supplementing it with entirely new arguments where the need arises.

We can now offer a sketch of the argument to be developed in the following pages. First, we will determine what types of justifications there are, fix the scope and limits of each, and explicate their structure. This will tell us what possibilities have to be considered in attempting to solve the problem. After this has been accomplished, we shall eliminate all but one, showing in each case why no justification of this type is possible. This, then, will constitute a reduction of the general problem of induction to a special case—the remaining type of justification. We will show that this special case is a necessary condition for the existence of a positive solution to the general problem. Once this has been done, we will prove that in this special case no justification is possible because there can be no construction capable of jointly satisfying the conditions of the problem. The reduction will be carried out in such a way that the essential features of the general problem are embodied in the special case so that there is no need to explain why the special case is representative. If our argument is sound, then it will follow that the problem is finally solved. By way of a conclusion we will discuss certain of the philosophical ramifications of a solution of the problem, especially the issue of conventionalism.

CHAPTER TWO

On the Nature of Justification

2.1. This chapter concerns justification, not the word but the activity of using words to provide sufficient reason for a knowledge claim, belief, attitude, act, evaluation, or whatever may be the subject of a critical charge. It offers a theory of justification which explains what types there are and how they work. As in the case of such words as "logic," "probability," and "electricity," so in the case of "justification" and its associated forms we stand to learn more of theoretical significance by investigating the nature of the referent than by studying the way the word behaves in our language. Language often provides clues and suggests approaches, but the facts decide.

The theory we shall present is not new, although it makes certain novel distinctions. Our interest is focused on exhibiting the logical structure of the types of answers which may be legitimately submitted to fulfil requests for a justification. As we mentioned at the conclusion of the previous chapter, this focus is necessary because unless we know in what ways justifications can be constructed, and by what criteria we judge in each case whether the reasons adduced deserve acceptance, there is no assurance that each possibility for a justification has been considered.

2.2 Asking someone to say how he knows what he claims to know, why he believes what he believes, why he evaluates the way he evaluates, why he acts the way he acts, etc., is the same as requesting him to justify his knowledge claim, his belief, his evaluation, his act, etc., whenever the request is a request for reasons. His justification is the reasons he gives in defense of his claim, belief, evaluation, act, etc. These reasons are adequate, and thus constitute a satisfactory justification, if they are sufficient as a defense. If not, they may be a partial justification or none at all.

Sometimes justifications do not consist in presenting reasons. We justify trust more by what we do than by what we say, and thus with another's confidence, his respect, his interest, his cautiousness, or his dislike. But we mention this case so that we may pass over it.

The kind of justification relevant in connection with the problem of induction, and thus the kind for which this chapter has been set aside, is the procedure of adducing reasons for accepting a certain claim, belief, evaluation, or act. This procedure is argumentation, and so we shall henceforth take a justification to be an argument. Consequently, a justification begins with premises which, at least for the sake of the argument, are granted by the parties involved and proceeds, stepwise, by one or more inferences until a conclusion is reached which asserts, in effect, that what required justification is acceptable in terms of such criteria of acceptability as govern the case. This is not meant to imply that a justification need have anything like the form of a logical proof. What is intended is simply that a justification be subject to the same criteria for evaluating soundness and the same contextual requirements for precision and clarity.

Of course, not any set of reasons constitutes a justifying argument. They must be reasons which are acceptable in themselves. If they are acceptable, they transmit their acceptability to the conclusion for which they are premises by virtue of the link provided by the consequence relation. For in a valid argument the acceptability of the premises insures the acceptability of the conclusion. But what are and what are not acceptable reasons depends upon the particulars of the case. For example, in the case of the justification of a factual claim by empirical evidence, inductive evidence from past experience can be an acceptable reason for the claim; whereas, in the case of the problem of induction, such evidence is unacceptable as a reason. Justification thus assumes the existence of acceptable reasons which it is the task of the justifier to uncover and deploy against the critical charge. If nothing were acceptable, there would be nothing to use as a justificatory basis. But, likewise, justification assumes the existence of something which is, at least theoretically, unacceptable. If everything were theoretically acceptable, there would be nothing left to justify. Therefore, justification begins with a limited acceptance and ends by showing us where our commitments lie.

Our theory of justification follows, in rough outline, the recent investigations of Feigl into the logic of justification, and, in accord with his usage, we shall call what is to be justified the "justificandum" and what is to do the justifying the "justificans."[1] According to Feigl's account, the function of justification is to show in just what way accepting the justificans involves accepting the justificandum. He writes: "Justification consists in the disclosure (exhibition, demonstration) of a conformity of that which is to be justified (the *justificandum*) with a certain principle or set of principles which do the justifying (the *justificans*)."[2] But the notion of conformity employed here fails to explicate adequately the sort of thing which is disclosed in a justification. Let us put the matter in somewhat different terms: A justification is an argument form filled out with the justificans as premises and the justificandum (or a statement asserting the acceptability of the justificandum relative to certain conditions of adequacy) as conclusion, together with the inferential links connecting the conclusion to the premises. Of course, these links need not be spelled out in a particular case. Logical rigor often defers to obviousness. But they are crucial to showing in what way acceptance of the justificans involves acceptance of the justificandum.

The essence of Feigl's account of justification is his distinction between two basic types of justification. The first type he calls "validation"; the second, "vindication":

When we speak of "justification" we may have reference to the legitimizing of a knowledge-claim; or else we may have in mind the justification of an action. The first case may be called "justificatio cognitionis" (validation); the second, "justificatio actionis" (vindication). The rules of inductive and deductive inference serve as the justifying principles in validation; purposes together with (inductively confirmed or at least confirmable) empirical knowledge concerning means-ends relations, or in the extreme, degenerate case with purely logical truths, serve as the basis of vindication (pragmatic justification). Only ends can justify means, even if in accordance with the well known slogan it will be admitted that a given end may not justify the utilization of every means for its attainment.[3]

This characterization is less revealing than it might be, and in some ways it is incomplete. The modification we shall offer remedies these

---

[1] Cf. Feigl (9) and (10). The first of these articles is a lucid discussion of justification in the areas of logic, methodology, epistemology, and ethics, while the second confines itself to the area of ethics.

[2] Feigl (9), p. 121.   [3] Feigl (10), p. 674.

defects but retains the terms "validation" and "vindication" because they mark practically the same distinction in our version as they do in Feigl's.

By a validation we understand an argument which establishes the acceptability of not only knowledge-claims but also ethical and aesthetic evaluations, beliefs, attitudes, judgments, norms, principles, theses—in short, anything which can be formulated as a definite assertion and in terms of which disagreement is possible. The mode of justification peculiar to the case of validation is that of establishing the acceptability of the justificandum by subsuming it under a justificans each of whose components is acceptable quite independently of the justificandum. Something is validated when it is shown to follow from acceptable assumptions. By a vindication we understand an argument which establishes the acceptability of a certain action or policy of action relative to a particular end. This corresponds closely to Feigl's account, except that the latter is incomplete in one respect: in vindication a particular end is shown to justify the use of a certain means to attain it, but there are two senses in which a means may be justified by an end, and Feigl's account fails to distinguish between them. One we shall call "expediency vindication" and the other "preferability vindication."

By an expediency vindication we understand an argument which establishes the justificandum as a suitable means, in whatever sense is appropriate, to accomplish the desired end. For example, if a physician justifies his advice to take liver pills by arguing that they cure anemia, then he is offering an expediency vindication. The end is a cure of anemia, the means are liver pills, and the justificatory argument consists in whatever reasons are adduced to show that this means is properly adapted to achieving this end. These reasons may explain, by describing their physiological effects, how liver pills produce this cure, or they may simply prove by the weight of statistical evidence that such a cure results from taking liver pills. An expediency vindication provides in the means a sufficient condition for achieving the desired end, but it does not provide a necessary condition for it, nor does it show that the means in question are the best ones.

The preferability vindication also provides a sufficient condition. But this type of vindication closes the possibility left open by the expediency vindication—that some other means may be equally well adapted to accomplish the desired end. Thus by a preferability vindication we understand an argument which establishes the justificandum as the preferable means for achieving the end. What is shown is that no other means can achieve the end in a more adequate fashion than can the justificandum. The justificandum is, then, a necessary condition for achieving the end in the most desirable way. This is to say, of course, that what is shown by a preferability vindication is that the justificandum is the best means, in whatever sense of "best" is appropriate in the circumstances. In terms of the preceding example, the physician would be offering a preferability vindication were he to argue that "there's nothing like liver pills for relieving anemia." The physician might base his claim on the contention that liver pills bring relief faster than other forms of medication; that they have no harmful aftereffects, whereas all other medications do; or that they alone bring permanent relief. But, regardless of what basis he employs, he must exhibit the advantage of using the justificandum over the use of other possible means. This implies that a preferability vindication involves some standard of preferability and that its justificans contains reasons sufficient to show that, in terms of the standard, the justificandum is correctly rated best when compared to all other means available.

One point worth bearing in mind for future reference is that an argument which demonstrates that a justificandum is a necessary condition—but only a necessary condition—for achieving the relevant end is not a real vindication. The reason for this is obvious. If some means is shown to be a necessary but not sufficient condition for attaining an end, then what is proved is that if any means whatsoever can attain this end these means must succeed, or, conversely, that all means must fail if these means must. But, since it has not been established that any means will, in fact, succeed, it may well be that all means will fail. If we were to take as justified such means as can only be shown to be necessary conditions for attaining an end, we would occasionally have to say that a means is justified even though it stands not the slightest chance of accomplishing the end.

Thus a vindication requires three things. First, a specific ends and means. These are commonly fixed by the justificatory context, so that there is no quarrel about them. Second, criteria for determining the conditions under which the means is to be regarded as either suitable to achieving the end or preferable to any other means for achieving the end. Often such criteria are predetermined by the justificatory context, since the charge occasioning the justificatory argument normally employs such criteria to state its criticism. Sometimes, however, such criteria are not explicit, and proposals for the use of certain criteria may become controversial. Third, a vindication requires adequate reasons to establish the means in question as either suitably adapted or preferable when judged by such criteria. Since showing that the justificandum is suitably adapted or preferable in the respect specified by such criteria is the main burden of a vindicative argument, it is these reasons, as a rule, that are criticized whenever a vindicative argument is questioned. If, for example, the physician's advice were criticized by the retort, "But liver pills actually cause anemia," it would be these reasons—the rationale behind taking the justificandum as a satisfactory means to the end— which were impugned. Normally, this type of criticism arises more frequently than charges leveled against the criteria, for example, such as "Who cares about aftereffects?" "Who cares whether relief is faster than with other medications?" "Who cares about permanent relief?"

Let us sharpen somewhat the difference between validation and vindication. It must be made clear that they are independent forms of justification and that there is no general method for transforming a validation into a vindication and vice versa. This must be shown because we need to argue that, if a validation of induction is ruled out, this does not *ipso facto* rule out a vindication. Later we will see that, although Hume's argument eliminates the possibility of a validation of induction, the possibility of a vindication still remains.

Let us begin the clarification of this difference by introducing a technical expression. We will say of an assertion that it *holds in its domain* if, and only if, it satisfies the conditions for validity in its domain. That is, if it is an assertion in logic, it must be a logical truth; if it is an assertion in mathematics, it must be mathematically true; if it is an assertion in empirical science, it must be factually true; if it is an assertion in ethics, an evaluation, a norm, a maxim, a prescription, a moral criticism, or a normative theory, it must be ethically right; if it is an assertion in aesthetics, it must be aesthetically sound; and so forth. In these terms the requirement we made that the components of a justificans each be acceptable is now interpreted as the demand that each hold in its respective domain.

Now we can show that a spade is a spade and not a filled-out club. If we look at the whole spectrum of ends for which a justificandum may be utilized, we see an indefinitely large number of possibilities. For instance, a scientific law may be used as a component in a technique of measurement, as a principle of instrument construction, as an inference license, as a compact summary of an immense class of diverse phenomena, as a definition of certain concepts, as an explanation, or as a fundamental principle in a theoretical system.[4] But, more significantly for our purposes, it may be used also as a standard of achievement for other sciences, as an illustration of the poverty of its branch of science, as a method of complicating an issue, as a way of impressing others with one's erudition, as a means of ending boring cocktail-party conversation, or as an example of creativity. And in very many cases a justificandum need not hold in its domain in order to be well adapted or preferable for obtaining a particular end. Euclidean geometry is not a true characterization of physical space, but it can be vindicated as a useful device for surveyors. Inconsistencies can be vindicated as a suitable way of obfuscating an issue which is dangerously close to reaching clarity. Lies can be vindicated as a means of preventing nice old ladies from learning unhappy truths about their loved ones. One could go on. But, likewise, a justificandum may be such as to hold in its domain and yet be perfectly useless except in trivial cases (e.g., as an example of something which is completely trivial). Here the reader may pick his favorite platitude or dull fact—perhaps, "Some people are lucky." What this shows is that validation and vindication divide in terms of a crucial difference. Validations are required to establish that the justificandum holds in its domain, but vindications not only are not required to establish this but may be successful even though it is well known that the justificandum does *not* hold in its domain. They are required to show only that the justificandum has the pragmatic virtue of achieving, or most adequately achieving, a certain desired end. Therefore, there may be no possibility of validating a particular justificandum, but this does not mean that there is no way to vindicate it. The existence of a validation is not a necessary condition for the existence of a vindication.

2.3. It is sometimes charged that theories of justification represent particular attempts at justification in too abstract a form, thus neglecting the subtle dynamics and extreme complexity of actual situations. Such a charge is based on fact. It is true that separating

---

[4] Hanson (14), chap. v, offers an enlightening discussion of the many distinct uses a law may have within a particular branch of a science.

and theoretically reconstructing the interwoven dialectical moves entail some distortion of what actually goes on in real situations. But only a complete tape recording with motion pictures taken from each angle will prevent distortion. Theories by their very nature are selective, and theories of justification are selective because they attend only to what is relevant to the question, "Quid juris?"

Feigl's reply to this charge of artificiality is that

all logical analysis from Aristotle through Descartes down to our time necessarily consists of an artificial and schematic reconstruction, and its illuminating character depends precisely upon the disentanglements of factors or aspects which, though admittedly *fused* in ordinary argument, are in danger of being *con*fused in philosophical reflection.[5]

This reply seems quite adequate. Had the great logicians of the past and present—Aristotle, Boole, Frege, Hilbert, Russell, and Gödel, to cite the most prominent examples—not pressed the sort of analysis this criticism finds objectionable, we would know very little about the nature of sound argumentation. But perhaps polemical replies are not the best way of convincing the person who feels strongly that reconstruction leads to artificiality. Let us try an analogy.

Consider a lawyer who is appealing his client's case to a higher tribunal in order to void the unfavorable decision of a lower court on the grounds that the court showed bias against his client. The lawyer will be concerned not with all the events which transpired during the first trial but only with those relevant to his goal of getting the higher court to set aside the verdict. Suppose he chooses to argue that, while his client's case was very strong, the prosecutor's was so weak that only prejudice on the part of the jury could explain the adverse verdict. Then he will reconstruct the proceedings of the first trial selectively so as to concentrate upon such factors as bring out the strength of his client's case and the weakness of the prosecution's. If he is to maximize the chances of convincing the higher-court justices that his client actually received an unjust verdict, he will have to reconstruct the arguments both he and the prosecuting attorney presented at the first trial in such a way that all extraneous courtroom banter, all redundancies, all *ad hominem* remarks, all irrelevant aspects of the witnesses' testimony and behavior, all the various and sundry courtroom formalities and conventions—in short, all things which have no bearing on the logic of the two arguments as deter-

[5] Feigl (10), p. 676.

mined by the legal framework—are omitted from his presentation. The resulting account will differ radically from the course of events in the first trial. He may even reformulate the order in which his points were originally made to give more coherence to the new version; transform inexactitudes into more precise expressions to make the new version more lucid; tighten up his argumentation by, wherever possible, replacing loose pieces of reasoning with more cogent counterparts; redistribute some of the evidence so that the factual support of his case appears in its best light; explain features which may bear on how certain points were interpreted by the court; and systematize, simplify, reinterpret, and do many other things to increase his chances for a favorable verdict from the higher court. Clearly, the result will bear only a partial resemblance to the course of events during the first trial.

A reporter or a feature writer would have to be more faithful to the facts, but a lawyer is concerned not with human interest but only with the interests of one human. The philosopher is presumably even more disinterested. His interest, so far as justification is concerned, is in constructing a theory which, when applied to particular cases, explains in what way and how well these cases deal with their question, "Quid juris?" Consequently, in order to achieve his purpose, the philosopher, like the lawyer, deviates substantially from the actual events. The analysis which results fails to give an accurate recording of these events—but it could only succeed in doing so by failing to achieve its objective.

A single phenomenon occurs: two persons have an argument. Since the physicist, the biologist, the psychologist, the economist, the moralist, the poet, and the philosopher each slices experience differently, they each attend to different aspects and conceptualize by relating different properties. The physicist attends to sound waves, forces, counterforces, stresses and strains; the biologist, to muscular co-ordination, adrenal secretion, tissue damage; the psychologist, to needs, motives, frustrations, aggressions; the economist, to utilities, gain strategies, supply-demand interaction; the moralist, to virtues and vices; the poet, to love and hate; and the philosopher, in so far as there is one, to the logic of the argument.

In practice justificatory arguments possess a certain open-endedness. They can be extended by accommodating more and more general reasons so that, in fact, almost every justificatory argument is potentially a hierarchical justificatory scheme. Undoubtedly, everyone has had the experience of being called on to provide, step by step, progressively more encompassing principles to meet criticism directed at what was previously regarded as secure. This was the common experience of Socrates' interlocutors. But, at times, the Socratic mood comes upon us, and we find reasons to become unsatisfied with the sanction provided by "first-order" principles in another's justificatory argument.

If someone were to try to justify a criticism of something we had done by arguing that it was wrong because it was stealing, we might very well remain unmoved by this censure if we thought it an unacceptable guide to action in this kind of case. We might then require our critic to justify the application of his principle, leaving him the option of meeting our demands, showing us why his principle should hold in all cases of a type which includes ours, appealing to another norm, or withdrawing the reprimand. Of course, the critic might not take our criticism of his criticism seriously. Had we replied by saying that stealing little things does not matter, he would be right in doing so. But had we argued that, though what we did is properly called "stealing," what we did was right because in its owner's hands the article would have been put to bad use, our reply would have to be taken seriously. If, in order to get us to accept the condemnation, the critic were to argue that, nevertheless, the article benefits us and that the person who lost it was, so far, innocent, and that, thus, being an act which benefits the agent at the expense of the innocent, it is morally wrong, he would have produced a justification himself. But we might again switch to his role and, as critic, argue, in a utilitarian vein, that it is right to benefit ourselves and harm the innocent if this is the only way of securing the most happiness for the greatest number of persons. Against this, the critic might retort by arguing that the greatest happiness is sometimes a function of a huge number of trivially small pleasures on the part of a large number of people and a single excruciating pain on the part of a single person. Here the argument may take a decidedly theoretical turn or may return to the particular case to proceed as a disagreement over whether our victim was so badly victimized.

This example illustrates the open-endedness of the justificatory arguments: how arguments can accommodate higher-level reasons and become multitiered. The open-endedness of justificatory arguments may be omitted in reconstruction without incurring a sin of omission if, for example, the focus of interest is on invalidating the whole by invalidating one of its parts. Analogously, temporal development may be omitted, since it is irrelevant to soundness.

The importation of higher- and higher-level reasons may be reflected in an analysis which reconstructs the entire argument as a sequence of interlocking, though separate, arguments; or it may be obscured by an analysis which reconstructs the argument as a single multitiered argument. In the latter case, where order of development conflicts with the order of the tiers, precedence is given the order of tiers on the assumption that this order presents the argument at its best. Which approach we choose depends on what we wish to do. But, regardless of which is chosen, there will be a specific justificans and justificandum connected by a validative or vindicative argument. The only requirement imposed is that the number of separate reasons involved be finite, that is, either that the number of tiers be finite or that the number of interlocking arguments be finite. This requirement accords well with the fact that giving reasons must terminate with some reason not legitimately or relevantly subsumable under or vindicated in terms of other reasons. There must always come a point when it is no longer possible to push the question back and supplant disputed norms or principles by more general ones. On pain of infinite regress, we recognize the inevitability of a choice between the alternatives of accepting some justifying reason without further justification, simply rejecting it, or withdrawing from the controversy without having arrived at agreement, thus contenting ourselves with a stalemate. Every request for justification assumes the existence of some reasons without which the request either makes no sense or is merely a prelude to a *reductio* of the assumption that such reasons exist. There is, then, a limit to the generality of reasons which can legitimately be invoked in a particular type of argument, and this limit imposes a terminus for retrogressive criticism.

Likewise, though in concrete situations arguments are built up through the dynamic process of criticism and countercriticism, they are properly assessed by the statics of logic and evidential weight. The subtle, shifting interplay of thesis, antithesis, and synthesis is eliminated as complication to this assessment, and so is all trace of whether something played the role of stimulus or response. What remains is only what is of interest in assessing the worth of these arguments by the detached, abstract standards of argumentative soundness.

Furthermore, the complexity in the actual justificatory proceedings is minimized as far as possible. All complexity is removed whose removal leaves the structure of the argument intact. Thus what is lost is no loss to the philosopher.

2.4. The job of justifying a claim has its occupational hazards, but these are nothing new, since justification is distinguished from other uses of argumentation only by its particular purpose. They are, however, worth looking at. First, we shall review the safeguards, and then we shall examine the one hazard most frequently met in attempts to justify.

Three things are required to safeguard a justification. One is that the conclusion of the argument be entailed by its premisses. This determines whether the support offered on behalf of the justificandum is conclusive. Nonetheless, we sometimes sensibly accept a justificatory argument even though, as it stands, its conclusion is not implied by its premisses. How can this be, it may be asked, when, according to what has been said, this means that the acceptability possessed by the premisses is, in this instance, not transmitted to the conclusion?

The answer is that it would be sensible to accept the conclusion on the partial grounds afforded by the premisses if there is an explicit or implicit promissory note pledging further premisses which would make the presently incomplete justificans entail the conclusion and if it is sensible to believe that this note will turn out redeemable. Of course, there may be other conditions under which it would also be sensible tentatively to accept the conclusion, but we may disregard this case. If we knew there could be no such supplementation, then a full justification relative to the partial grounds provided by the incomplete premisses would indeed be impossible. Moreover, if we knew that these grounds are the only possible or legitimate starting point for such a justification, we would have to grant the impossibility, in principle, of such a justification. This, however, would not necessarily mean that the justificandum is unacceptable or that using it to obtain some end is a sign of irrationality. As long as there is no justification of a claim which is incompatible with it, countenancing it or abiding by it becomes a matter of choice describable, perhaps, as the choice of an "ultimate presupposition" or "first principle." Be this as it may, however, the essential point here is that, although ostensibly there seems to be no difference between a fallacious argument and an inconclusive one, there may, in fact, be a world of difference between them. There is a world of difference between accepting Goldbach's conjecture on the partial grounds afforded by the cases in which it can be verified and the theorems of Schnirelmann and Vinogradoff, and accepting the conclusion that anyone searching for Goldbach should not look in Mississippi because mathematicians are seldom found there.

The entailment requirement leads immediately to the second safeguard. This is that the premisses of the argument must be mutually consistent. It is clear that the entailment requirement itself makes sense only if this further requirement is satisfied, since, otherwise, the former requirement could always be fulfilled in a degenerate way, with the consequence that everything could be justified, even contradictory claims.

The third safeguard is the requirement that the premisses each be acceptable in that they hold in their domain. The satisfaction of this requirement is, as it were, the guaranty that there exists acceptability to be transferred to the justificandum via the links between it and the reasons adduced in the justificans.

The one hazard which crops up most frequently in connection with attempts to justify is the fallacy known as *petitio principii*, or "vicious circularity." The motivation behind the refusal to countenance arguments containing a *petitio principii* is not, as is often thought, the desire to rule out trivial justifications.[6] Trivial justifications are, in fact, justifications, though trivial ones. The real motivation is the desire not to allow the procedure of justification to become meaningless by allowing everything to be justified. If there were no prohibition against the fallacy of *petitio principii*, any claim whatsoever could be validated merely by inferring it from itself by $p \supset p$. But, unfortunately, many writers have construed this prohibition to be purely formal in character. Accordingly, their versions of this prohibition take the form of a stipulation requiring that the justificandum should not appear *literally* or *explicitly* as a component of the justificans. The reason that such formulations are untenable is that what counts as literal or explicit appearance is determined by whether the justificandum can be inferred directly by $p \supset p$. This leads to indefinitely many counterinstances where, instead of using $p \supset p$, we use such inference schemas as $([p \lor q] \ \& \ [p \lor \smallsmile q]) \supset p$.[7] Here,

---

[6] Even so careful an analyst as Feigl makes this mistake (see Feigl [9], p. 153).

[7] I am indebted to Professor C. G. Hempel for this example, which he suggested to me in conversation.

though the inference is strictly circular, p does not appear literally or explicitly in the premises. It might be suggested that we rule out any inference schema whose antecedent is logically equivalent to its consequent, but this would not help matters because it would leave counterinstances of the form $(p \ \& \ q) \supset p$, which cannot be ruled out on strictly formal grounds without either incurring more difficulties or ruling out legitimate inference schema. This shows that the question here is not solely a logical one. In a sense, every valid argument is circular, even quite significant ones. For the conclusion of a valid argument is logically contained in its premises, though, in many cases, absent psychologically.[8] However, if we abandon the attempt to characterize the *petitio principii* in purely formal terms, it is possible to state this prohibition without involving ourselves in such difficulties. A *petitio principii* occurs where there is no way to make the premises of a justificatory argument acceptable without first establishing the acceptability of the justificandum. That is to say, if in order to establish the acceptability of the justicans we have no recourse in the argument but to appeal to the justificandum, thereby tacitly assuming its acceptability, the argument commits a *petitio principii*. What is required is that one's doubts concerning the justificandum be peculiar to it and that they be resolved only by means of the enlightenment gained by exhibiting the logical chain linking it to a set of reasons each of which is antecedently acceptable. This being the case, we have required that a justificatory argument contain premises which are acceptable and a conclusion which is less than acceptable *in situ*. Given this, however, the prohibition against vicious circularity is seen to be built into the conditions which define the justificatory context, for any argument which contains this fallacy will *ipso facto* fail to conform to what we have required of a justificatory argument. Such a fallacious argument will violate these conditions in one or the other direction. If the conclusion is, as required, less than acceptable *in situ*, then at least one premise (the one for which the acceptability of the conclusion is a necessary condition) will itself be less than acceptable. If the premises are each acceptable, as required, then, because the acceptability of at least one depends directly upon the acceptability of the conclusion, the

---

[8] Logic often leads to results which we were unaware we were committed to by accepting the premises of an argument. Thus it is frequently said that a certain conclusion is logically contained in a set of premises, though, psychologically, it is not (see Hempel [15], pp. 234–35).

conclusion will be acceptable *in situ.* Thus in the case of such a fallacy there is no justification either because the justificandum never needed it or because the justificans could never give it.

2.5. Justification is not, as is believed by some, argumentation based upon an area of agreement and an area of disagreement which proceeds by extending the former to encompass some item or items in the latter. We do not establish the acceptability of a claim by agreeing that it is valid, and we do not establish its unacceptability by agreeing that it is invalid. Nor do we preclude justification when we agree to disagree. Thus it is not agreement, or acceptability to the persons involved, which amounts to almost the same thing, but, rather, the acceptability of an assertion by virtue of its holding in its domain which marks something as a legitimate starting point for a justification. Further, justification is not absorbing something outside the sphere of what is acceptable into that sphere, because a justifiable claim was always acceptable in its domain or as a means to a chosen end. If not, there could be no true justification. Thus the correct model for the procedure of justification is not osmosis but the demonstration that what is implicitly contained in the reasons we correctly accept must *ipso facto* itself be accepted.

This concludes what we have to say about justification. In the course of what we have said, we presented a theory of the nature of justification which delineated the alternatives open to the prospective justifier of induction and to the would-be skeptic, which described how each alternative works, which marked the conditions of adequacy for each, and which disclosed the differences between them. This theory adopted some old distinctions and introduced some new ones. It answered some questions and left some unanswered. It explained certain features of justification and left others unexplained. And it analyzed certain concepts but not others. Admittedly, then, what we have said is less than a full portrait. We have gone into some degree of detail but by no means as much as would be required of a study limited solely to the topic of justification. Yet none of the things left undone, the questions left unanswered, the features left unexplained, the concepts left unanalyzed, needed to be done to achieve our professed aim.

CHAPTER THREE

The Reduction of the General Problem

3.1. Throughout the post-Humean phase of modern philosophy the number of different types of solutions which have been proffered for the problem of induction is small, though there have been a large number of instances of each type. It has been claimed that induction is, like the principles and theorems of logic and pure mathematics, valid on strictly deductive grounds. It has been claimed that induction follows from the principle of the uniformity of nature and derives its validity from that principle. It has been claimed that induction is one of the fundamental principles by which the human mind operates and so is synthetic a priori. It has been claimed that induction is an empirically derived rule which is supported by overwhelming evidence from past experience. It has been claimed that induction is pragmatically preferable to any other way of making predictions because it will certainly reveal regularities if they exist in nature. It has been claimed that induction's validity is self-evident to the intuition. And so on, for a few, but not many, more types.

One way a skeptic might proceed, and the way most skeptics have actually proceeded, would be to take up each of these "solutions" in turn and present refutations for each. Thus the skeptic argues that the first falls prey to the Humean criticism that any attempt to construe induction as a deductive rule turns inductive inferences into *non sequiturs;* that the second, even assuming that this principle makes sense, does nothing but beg the question; that the third is wholly unsupported and nearly wholly unclear; that the fourth commits a *petitio principii;* that the fifth is inconclusive; and that the sixth is merely a declaration of philosophical bankruptcy. But this approach has serious drawbacks. One has to examine, one by one, a sizable number of particular arguments and find a refutation for each separately. Thus one has to consider numerous bad arguments, retrace familiar ground by examining familiar arguments and reformulating familiar refutations, and become involved in one side issue after another. Hence this approach would have the great philosophical disadvantage of being exceedingly tedious. Moreover, with this approach one has no assurance, even after a very fastidious search, that one has not missed an argument or that one will not in the future discover some new argument suffciently different from those now existing to raise the problem of induction anew. Hence this approach fails, in principle, to yield a satisfactory solution of the problem. The desirability of an alternative approach is, therefore, evident.

What is required is that we be more systematic. The approach we shall adopt will be fully systematic in the sense that, if the arguments we use are sound, there will be no possibility that a type of justificatory argument is missed or that a new type may be discovered to raise the problem anew.

Our approach will be to reduce the general problem of induction to a special case success in which is a necessary condition for a positive solution to the general problem. This will be done by eliminating all types of arguments but one, which will, then, constitute the special case. Then we shall prove that a justification of the kind required in this special case is impossible. In the present chapter we carry out the reduction, while in the next we take the final step in the argument.

3.2. As will be recalled, our last formulation of the problem of induction was in terms of the question, "What, if anything, justifies our belief in the reliability of inductively framed predictions and generalizations and our disbelief in non-inductive predictions and generalizations?" Non-demonstrative inference was characterized as inference from a sample to its population, and inductive inference was found to be one among indefinitely many forms of such inference. Inductive projections from sample to population were observed to be projections of regularities, whereas non-inductive projections were observed to be projections of irregularities. We described two events as forming a regularity if the occurrence of the first was invariably associated with the occurrence of the second and if this association constitutes the simplest such association in the sample. Induction posited the persistence of regularities. Now we may make two modifications before we provide a statement of the general problem of induction. First, we should explicitly include statistical regularities. Second, we should begin to talk in terms of the projection of hypotheses. Accordingly, we may say that induction frames hypotheses of two kinds: lawful hypotheses of the form 'All instances of P_1 are instances of P_2' and statistical hypotheses of the form 'The probability of a P_1 being a P_2 is φ'. It is to be understood that only lawful hypotheses imply consequences about particular individuals or about finite classes of such individuals.[1] Also we may interpret the probability value as specifying the proportion of P_1's that are P_2's or, for those familiar with the frequency interpretation of the concept of probability, as specifying the limit of the relative frequencies as n goes to infinity.

For the purpose of stating the general problem of induction, we shall not try to make things more precise, because no increase in precision materially affects the character of this problem. This can be demonstrated easily. The problem of induction is the problem of finding adequate reasons for choosing one method of projection instead of other methods or for showing that no such reasons exist. A non-inductive method can be defined in terms of induction as a method for projecting systematic deviations, but also induction can be defined in terms of any non-inductive method as a method for projecting certain systematic deviations. What is important to the problem is the absolute difference or contrast between types of projections. This difference will merely be sharpened by any refinement of these methods. Because these methods of non-demonstrative inference are interdefinable, whatever is relevant to refining the inductive method is, therefore, relevant to refining the non-inductive methods. Making our formulation of the inductive method or, for that matter, each of the non-inductive methods more precise only makes the problem more precise. It does not change it.

The general problem of induction has already been stated in many versions, but here, at the outset of its reduction, it is convenient to bring them together in a form which clearly displays its full generality. Applying a non-demonstrative rule to a sample results in a hypothesis about the members of the population not included in the sample. Of course, some inferences from a sample extend only to a limited number of the unknown members, but we shall neglect these.[2]

---

[1] This difference between lawful and statistical hypotheses is widely noted (see Nagel [23], pp. 393–402, or Reichenbach [32], pp. 337–52).

[2] Because such forms of inductive inference, for our purposes, involve no further complications (see von Wright [40], pp. 1–3).

Such hypotheses represent projections from what we know to what is not yet known. Some take the form of assertions that all cases which satisfy the condition P_1 satisfy the condition P_2, while some take the form of assertions that for all cases which satisfy P_1 the probability of their satisfying P_2 is such-and-such. Since the scientist must decide upon a hypothesis in advance of a knowledge of whether it truthfully characterizes each case it covers, he must project. Each method of projection, inductive and non-inductive alike, offers him a hypothesis which, by its own standards, conforms to the sample that forms the basis of his projection. Each offers its own standard for correction should subsequent testing disprove its former projection. Each is, therefore, a closed system. The general problem of induction is, then, the question of whether from outside of every such system we can say why one system rather than another should be chosen.

3.3. The theory of justification presented in the last chapter suggests a natural way of performing the reduction. If the theory is correct, there are only two ways in which a principle such as induction can be justified. Either it can be validated or it can be vindicated or it cannot be justified at all. Thus, if validation can be ruled out, the problem reduces to a vindicative one, and, if there is a particular type of vindicative argument whose success is a necessary condition of the possibility of any vindication, there is only one type of vindicative argument which needs to be considered. This type, then, constitutes the special case of the reduction. Furthermore, if it is shown that, in principle, no vindicative argument of this form can succeed in offering a satisfactory justification, then we will have demonstrated that induction cannot be justified. This will be our approach, and, in line with it, we now turn to the first step of the reduction—the elimination of validation as a contender.

Since this is a discussion of the problem of induction, it is not unusual that we find ourselves turning to Hume for our point of departure. Hume's conclusion that we have no epistemological warrant to believe that knowledge of the past gives any clue to what the future will be like was derived from his famous skeptical polemic which may be summarized and modernized in the form of the following dilemma —henceforth to be referred to as "Hume's dilemma." The first horn is:

If a proposed justificatory argument A attempts to establish the formal validity of induction by trying to deduce it from a set of purely logical or mathematical statements, that is, if A claims that inductive conclusions are necessarily true providing only that their premisses are true and they follow by correct applications of inductive rules, then *A* is a *non sequitur* because the implication of the premisses in an inductive argument with their conclusion cannot be a logical or mathematical truth. Since the conclusion of an inductive argument always says more than its premisses, no such defense as this can justify induction.

The second horn of Hume's dilemma is:

If a proposed justificatory argument *A* attempts to establish the soundness of induction by trying to prove it on the basis of past experience, a principle of the uniformity of nature, or another inductive rule, that is, if *A* claims that inductive inferences are warranted because they have been successful in the past, because nature is limited in variety, or because they are justified by some other inductive rule, then *A* commits a *petitio principii*, for such justificatory arguments merely assume what they are required to prove. The argument that success in the past implies future success and the argument using the principle of the uniformity of nature both are viciously circular in that the acceptability of their premisses depends upon the acceptability of induction. And the argument which imports another inductive principle merely trades on the possibility of alternative formulations of the principle of induction, thus begging the question. Hence, any argument *A* which tries to justify induction in these ways must fail to provide a justification.

Given these horns, the argument concludes as follows:

But, since every argument purporting to justify induction must be either of the type considered in the first horn or the type considered in the second, every such argument must be fallacious, which is just another way of saying that induction cannot be justified.

Two points concerning this dilemma deserve mention before we proceed to its consequences. First, Hume's dilemma asserts, in part, that an attempt to justify induction which argues that induction will be successful in the future because it was successful in the past is viciously circular. This criticism assumes that the argument it criticizes draws its conclusion that induction will be successful in the future by an *induction* from a sample consisting of past inductive successes. Strictly speaking, however, this need not be so. Instead of employing induction itself to draw this conclusion, one might use a slightly different method, though not one which is too different. So long as one employs a method that is not so counterinductive as to contradict the very conclusion one wishes to draw, one may escape the charge of strict circularity. But this would be a hollow victory. This maneuver does not constitute a way out of the dilemma, because importing another method merely shifts the question to what sanctions inferences by this method. The new method would have to remain without any support on pain of circularity or infinite regress, depending upon whether the regress returns to a method which has been previously used or not. Of course, somewhere along the regress something of a different and more substantial character might be offered, but this *would* be something different and would change the argument to something different.

Second, there is a stronger criticism than blatant circularity that can be made against the use of principles such as uniformity of nature. Generalizations asserting the over-all regularity or limited independent variety[3] of nature contain an ambiguity which can be removed only at the price of making such principles totally useless as part of a justificatory argument. This ambiguity appears immediately if we ask how we know whether what induction projects as a regularity is the kind of thing which such principles say remains uniform. How do we know in particular cases that inductive projections are what, according to such principles, we are assured will persist? Unless we can determine this, we have no better reason for invoking such principles to affirm the validity of induction than we have for invoking them to deny its validity. But, to determine this, we must find out which past uniformities these principles assert will endure and which they assert will not. There are only two types of replies to this question. One is that the set of all past regularities is the set of exactly those regularities which will endure, and the other is that it is some proper subset of this set. But, as Hempel has pointed out,[4] if such principles are construed in accordance with the first type of reply so that they project *all* past regularities, then they lead to inconsistency because they will project incompatible hypotheses. If such principles are construed in accordance with the second type of reply, we must ask how we are to distinguish the proper subset of all and only those regularities which should be projected. Notice, however, that we cannot include in this set any hypotheses which are false, that is, any regularities which will break down, for this would falsify the principle of the uniformity of nature and make utter nonsense of its use in a justificatory argument. Hence we must formulate

[3] Keynes (20), chap. xxii.

[4] Hempel's observation is contained in an unpublished paper.

44

this principle so that it directs that those and only those past regularities which remain stable in the future are countenanced as uniformities. But this makes the principle an empty tautology because now all it asserts is that those regularities which persist are the ones which persist and that those which do not are the ones which do not. This is hardly the sort of principle which is useful to include in a justificatory argument.

Hume's dilemma stood for approximately one hundred and eighty years of vigorous philosophical activity without having a single forceful objection brought against it.[5] This is no accident. Hume's dilemma does prove something definite, though not what Hume and many Humean skeptics thought. Hume's dilemma is a conclusive refutation of any possibility that induction can be validated, but no more. And we shall use it as such to accomplish the first step of our reduction.

For the most part, philosophers who have concerned themselves with the problem of induction have mistakenly identified validation and vindication because they failed to give their attention to the nature of justification. By failing to make this distinction, inductivists, until only recently, have continued to drape themselves on the horns of Hume's dilemma, while skeptics, with an air of complacency, have continued to echo the arguments of their illustrious predecessor. Even such careful thinkers as, for example, Ayer, Strawson, and Goodman

[5] Peirce, it is true, constructed a pragmatic argument for justifying induction which bears much similarity to the one Reichenbach later developed. Peirce's argument, however, did not become known until well after Reichenbach's views were already accepted as a serious challenge to Humean skepticism. Moreover, Peirce's ideas were by no means as adequately worked out as Reichenbach's. One may get some notion of just how far Peirce's ideas went from the following typical fragments: "The true guarantee of the validity of induction is that it is a method of reaching conclusions which, if persisted in long enough, will assuredly correct any error concerning future experience into which it may temporarily lead us" ([25], Vol. II, sec. 2.769) or "The justification for believing that an experimental theory which has been subjected to a number of experimental tests will be in the near future sustained as well by further such tests as it has hitherto been, is that by steadily pursuing that method we must in the long run find out how the matter really stands. The reason that we must do so is that our theory, if it be admissible even as a theory, simply consists in supposing that such experiments will in the long run have results of a certain character" ([25], Vol. V, sec. 170). Thus we note here that, well before Reichenbach, Peirce was in possession of the basic idea of a pragmatic argument; but we shall deal only with Reichenbach's work because it is fully developed and is widely known. The reader with a historical interest in the relationship between Peirce's and Reichenbach's work on a justification of induction may profitably consult the latter's contribution to the Schilpp volume on John Dewey, where this connection is discussed (31), pp. 188–90.

have been guilty of confusing validation and vindication. In his famous book *Language, Truth and Logic,* Ayer writes:

> There are only two ways of approaching this problem on the assumption that it is a genuine problem, and it is easy to see that neither of them can lead to its solution. One may attempt to deduce the proposition which one is required to prove either from a purely formal principle or from an empirical principle. In the former case one commits the error of supposing that from a tautology it is possible to deduce a proposition about a matter of fact; in the latter case one simply assumes what one is setting out to prove. . . . Thus it appears that there is no possible way of solving the problem of induction, as it is ordinarily conceived.[6]

This quotation shows that Ayer fails to consider the possibility of a vindicative argument. In a recent publication we find Strawson making the same mistake. "If it is said that there is a problem of induction, and that Hume posed it, it must be added that he solved it."[7] Goodman takes the same point of view, but, because his is a more detailed and careful analysis and because it has been widely acclaimed as the finishing touch, we shall give it special attention.

Goodman writes: "I think Hume grasped the central question and considered his answer to be passably effective. And I think his answer is reasonable and relevant, even if it is not entirely satisfactory."[8] However, it is clear from what Goodman later says that he means only that Hume's answer is not entirely satisfactory as an adequate explication of induction; that is, one which characterizes the distinction between acceptable and unacceptable predictions, not that it fails to do away with what he calls the "old problem"—what we are calling the general problem.[9] Goodman's own skeptical arguments are, in fact, only a modernization of Hume's. As Goodman argues it:

> If the problem is to explain how we know that certain predictions will turn out to be correct, the sufficient answer is that we don't know any such thing. If the problem is to *find* some way of distinguishing antecedently between true and false predictions, we are asking for prevision rather than for philosophical explanation. Nor does it help matters much to say that we are merely trying to show that or why certain predictions are *probable.* Often it is said that while we cannot tell in advance whether a prediction

[6] Ayer (1), p. 49.

[7] Strawson (37), pp. 20–21. The full version of Strawson's views on justifying induction are to be found in (36).

[8] Goodman (13), p. 64.

[9] "What Goodman later says" refers to his remarks in (13), pp. 65–68.

concerning a given throw of a die is true, we can decide whether the prediction is a probable one. But if this means determining how the prediction is related to actual frequency distributions of future throws of the die, surely there is no way of knowing or proving this in advance. On the other hand, if the judgment that the prediction is probable has nothing to do with subsequent occurrences, then the question remains in what sense a probable prediction is any better justified than an improbable one.

Now obviously the genuine problem cannot be one of attaining unattainable knowledge or of accounting for knowledge that we do not in fact have.[10]

What Goodman neglects is, therefore, what Hume neglects—that a justificatory argument need not try to show either that inductive predictions are true or that they are probable. To try to show this is to try to validate induction. But, by failing to see that a justificatory argument might take the form of a vindication, Goodman fails to argue against this possibility. Hence he is not warranted in concluding what he concludes here—that attempting to justify induction is attempting the impossible. The genuine problem is obviously not one of attaining the unattainable or accounting for something we do not have; Hume's argument shows this. But it may be that of showing that induction is a suitable or the best means of achieving reliable generalizations, assuming this is what we desire and that this is, in fact, possible.

Goodman's argument does not stop here, however. So we must carry ours further. What Goodman wishes to do next is to show that, properly understood, the problem of induction has nothing to do with justification in the traditional sense. His argument here is an argument by analogy from the case of deduction:

Principles of deductive inference are justified by their conformity with accepted deductive practice. Their validity depends upon accordance with the particular deductive inferences we actually make and sanction. If a rule yields inacceptable inferences, we drop it as invalid.[11]

But, he goes on to say, we justify particular deductive inferences by their conformity to the principles of deductive inference. This circularity, he argues, is virtuous. In his own defense he writes:

The point is that rules and particular inferences alike are justified by being brought into agreement with each other. *A rule is amended if it yields an inference we are unwilling to accept; an inference is rejected if it violates a rule we are unwilling to amend.* The process of justification is

[10] Goodman (13), pp. 65–66. [11] Goodman (13), p. 67.

the delicate one of making mutual adjustments between rules and accepted inferences; and in the agreement achieved lies the only justification needed for either.[12]

Assuming this characterization is accurate in the case of deduction, Goodman applies it forthwith to the case of induction. By way of establishing the analogue, he says:

> All this applies equally well to induction. An inductive inference, too, is justified by conformity to general rules, and a general rule by conformity to accepted inductive inferences. Predictions are justified if they conform to valid canons of induction; and the canons are valid if they accurately codify accepted inductive practice.[13]

But, because his analogy between deduction and induction does not hold, Goodman's conclusion that we can stop plaguing ourselves with the old-fashioned question of justification is not established. A rule of deductive inference, such as *modus ponens* or hypothetical syllogism, is a valid rule if, and only if, there is no instance where it sanctions an argument containing true premises and a false conclusion. A particular deductive inference is a valid inference if, and only if, its logical form is that of a valid argument schema which, in turn, possesses validity by virtue of the validity of the rules determining it. A rule of deductive inference or a sequence of interlocking rules formally represents infinitely many particular arguments. Such a rule is acceptable only if no argument it represents has true premises and a false conclusion. Particular inferences are acceptable only if they are represented by a valid rule or sequence of interlocking, valid rules or, what amounts to the same thing, only if there is no case of another particular inference whose logical form is exactly parallel and which contains true premises but a false conclusion. Contrary to Goodman's view, there is no circularity here, either vicious or virtuous. For there is a clear-cut criterion of validity with which to rationalize our acceptance or rejection of a rule or inference. It is a complete falsification of the deductive case to describe it as one in which we maintain rules so long as they do not conflict with inferences we are unwilling to reject and maintain inferences so long as they do not conflict with rules we are unwilling to amend. This would be flagrantly circular. The true description is that both rules and inferences are judged by the independent criterion of formal validity. Rules and inferences alike are acceptable only if they preserve truth under formal manipulation. If

[12] *Ibid.*   [13] *Ibid.*

a rule has an instance where it permits the inference of a false conclusion from true premises, it is not maintained. If an inference has a logical form which is such that there is another inference of the same form with true premises and a false conclusion, then it is not maintained. However, the case of induction is by no means analogous because there is no comparable criterion of validity. In the case of induction there is circularity which, in the context of Goodman's argument, is vicious, not virtuous. Though an inductive rule represents infinitely many particular inferences in the same way a deductive rule represents the inferences it formalizes, the analogy ends here. There being no independent criterion specifying what is meant by validity and how it is determined, this is truly a case in which we abandon rules which conflict with cherished inferences and abandon inferences which conflict with cherished rules. This may well be a correct description of the way things are in actual practice, but, if there is no criterion of validity, there is no non-circular way to determine whether the adjustments of rules to inferences and inferences to rules, which is characteristic of the inductive process, are better than those which might be made according to some non-inductive process. We have no non-circular way to tell whether adjustments made on an inductive basis tend toward the best system or not. Any sort of non-inductive rule, regardless how bizarre, can be adjusted to inferences which are equally bizarre, and vice versa. The basic point is that it is this very criterion of validity that is sought by those seeking to justify induction, so that, unless they are able to succeed, as Goodman insists they are not, there is no way for him to show that mutual adjustment of the inductive variety is by itself enough to produce valid rules and valid inferences in the long run. The inductivist will surely reply that, with a justification of induction, we have a criterion to distinguish valid rules and inferences from invalid ones and to rationalize our unwillingness to modify a rule or inference, whereas without one there is nothing to distinguish clearheadedness from hardheadedness. Goodman's analysis, as nothing more than an analysis of the explicatory process by which rules are continuously refined, is certainly a sensible one. But the argument for skepticism based upon it, having no convenient analogy for support, must be rejected because it has not shown that induction cannot be vindicated.

In the early 1930's Reichenbach proposed his now famous pragmatic justificatory argument, thus ending the one hundred and eighty years of substanceless speculation since Hume. One unique feature of

Reichenbach's approach which partly explains why his argument was not more of the same fruitless speculation is its acceptance of the fact that Hume was right about something. Reichenbach was the first philosopher to see that Hume's argument rules out the possibility of a validation of induction. Reichenbach initiated the idea of using an ends-means argument and clearly saw that this sort of argument was not eliminated by Hume's dilemma. This aspect of Reichenbach's argument, his polemic against a Humean solution of the problem, provides us with the reason why Hume's argument constitutes a refutation of the possibility that induction can be validated. Thus it gives us our first step toward the reduction. Reichenbach writes:

Hume started with the assumption that a justification of inductive inference is only given if we can show that inductive inference must lead to success. In other words, Hume believed that any justified application of the inductive inference presupposes a demonstration that the conclusion is true. It is this assumption on which Hume's criticism is based. His two objections directly concern only the question of the truth of the conclusion; they prove that the truth of the conclusion cannot be demonstrated. The two objections, therefore, are valid only in so far as the Humean assumption is valid. It is this question to which we must turn: Is it necessary, for the justification of inductive inference, to show that its conclusion is true.[14]

Then Reichenbach goes on to answer this question by saying:

A rather simple analysis shows us that this assumption does not hold. Of course, if we were able to prove the truth of the conclusion, inductive inference would be justified; but the converse does not hold: a justification of inductive inference does not imply a proof of the truth of the conclusion. The proof of the truth of the conclusion is only a sufficient condition for the justification of induction, not a necessary condition.[15]

To substantiate his denial of the assumption that validation is the only way of approaching the problem of induction, Reichenbach proceeds to argue for an alternative way of developing a justificatory argument:

The inductive inference is a procedure which is to furnish us the best assumption concerning the future. If we do not know the truth about the future, there may be nonetheless a best assumption about it, i.e., a best assumption relative to what we know. We must ask whether such a char-

[14] Reichenbach (30), p. 348.

[15] *Ibid.*

acterization may be given for the principle of induction. If this turns out to be possible, the principle of induction will be justified.[16]

This points the way toward a new type of justification, a vindication, which is not bound by the prohibitive condition that it be shown that inductive inference satisfies the sufficient condition of predictive success.

We must now finally settle the question of whether Hume's dilemma conclusively shows that induction is unjustifiable by validation. Stripped of all complications, the reason why this condition is prohibitive is that, to satisfy it, we require knowledge which can be gained only by the very procedures denied us by the nature of the problem. The knowledge we would require is such as would guarantee the truth of inductive conclusions or, what is virtually the same thing, guarantee predictive success. But here the guaranty can be only one of two types, for, in the domain of induction, truth is the only basis of acceptability. On the one hand, it can be a deductive guaranty, so that what is demanded of a validation is a demonstration that inductive conclusions are true necessarily whenever legitimately inferred from true premises. But this sort of guaranty is precluded by the first horn of Hume's dilemma. What is requisite is that induction be proved to be deduction. But that one defining characteristic of an inductive argument is non-demonstrativeness shows conclusively that no such assimilation can be made. Deductive arguments produce conclusions which never assert more than is logically contained in their premises, whereas inductive arguments produce conclusions which invariably assert more than their premises. On the other hand, the guaranty can be inductive, so that what is demanded of a validation is a demonstration that inductive conclusions are highly probable, have a greater probability of being true than do non-inductive conclusions, or have better evidential support. But this sort of guaranty is precluded by the second horn of Hume's dilemma. What is requisite is that induction be proved inductively sound. But this is viciously circular because, of necessity, the intended self-justifying application of induction can be no less in need of justification than any other application of induction. Hence, as long as the problem of induction is subject to the condition that a positive solution must show that induction establishes its conclusions as true, probably true, well enough supported, or the like, this problem is bound by an impossible condition.

[16] Reichenbach (30), pp. 348–49.

But it is only the construction of the problem as one of validation that binds it to this impossible condition. To validate a principle, its acceptability must be established by showing it is a consequence of acceptable assumptions. If it were possible to subsume induction under deductive or inductive canons, its acceptability would be established either by a demonstration of its deductive validity or by a demonstration of its inductive soundness. But it is not. And, since validation makes it necessary to show that the justificandum holds in its domain in order for it to be acceptable and since deductive validity and inductive soundness are the only two senses in which induction is said to hold in its domain, there can be no acceptable assumptions from which to derive induction. Were only a validation of induction sufficient to justify it, Hume's dilemma would be conclusive; but, as it is, there is a type of justification which can be successful without showing that induction holds in its domain.

Hence Hume's dilemma effectively eliminates the validation of induction, while, at the same time, leaving open the question of whether a policy of action in accord with induction might be vindicated in terms either of expediency or of preferability. The general problem of induction thus reduces to the subproblem of whether or not it is possible to vindicate induction.

3.4. This completes the first step of our reduction. What remains to be done is to show that induction can be vindicated only if it can be vindicated along the lines of one particular type of vindicative argument. The particular type of vindicative argument which will be the special case for our reduction is Reichenbach's argument. Thus we shall show that, if induction can be vindicated, the vindication must take the form of Reichenbach's pragmatic argument. The next step, then, is to take a look at that argument.

Reichenbach's argument was developed within the context of the frequency theory of probability. Reichenbach thought that this development gave him the advantage of a more exact and more general formulation of both the end and the means of his vindicative argument. Concerning the end with respect to which induction was to be vindicated, Reichenbach says:

> Scientific method pursues the aim of predicting the future; in order to construct a precise formulation for this aim we interpret it as meaning that scientific method is intended to find the limits of the frequency.[17]

[17] Reichenbach (32), p. 474.

The end, according to this quotation, is attaining knowledge of the limits of series of events whose frequency of occurrence converges to a limit. But this, as Reichenbach knew, would not satisfy many philosophers. For to say that the aim of scientific inquiry is the discovery of limits of the relative frequency in the long run immediately invites the reply which many of Reichenbach's critics have made, namely, that showing induction can find limits at some point in the infinite series has no argumentative import for finite scientists. One such critic has argued: "It is not too interesting to be told that induction is at least as good as any other method 'if pursued long enough'; for 'the long run' is a fiction without any definite empirical significance ('in the long run we are all dead' remarked the late Lord Keynes)."[18] But Reichenbach anticipated this criticism and forearmed himself by introducing the notion of a *practical limit*. In terms of this notion he offers an alternative construction for the end sought by science: the attainment of knowledge of limits of series of events whose frequency of occurrence exhibits sufficient convergence to be ascertained by mortal investigators. The practical limit is, according to Reichenbach, a concept which

refers to a sequence which reaches sufficient convergence after a fairly large number of elements, but which may diverge in later parts that lie beyond the reach of human experience. It is obvious that the rule of induction is justified, too, when the condition of the limit is replaced by that of a practical limit. The justification, in fact, will be improved, since finite attainability then means an attainability for human capacities. A sequence that converges so late that human observers cannot experience the convergence has, for all practical purposes, the character of a sequence without a limit.[19]

Unfortunately, Reichenbach here opens himself to an objection which is not crucial to his argument and which can easily be avoided. As he defines it, the practical limit need not coincide with the true limit of the sequence, since, according to Reichenbach's account, divergence of any sort from the practical limit can occur in parts of the sequence outside the reach of human experience. Reichenbach's general views on science led him to stress predictability within the area of human experience, but many philosophers of science would stress the discovery of truths as a more central concern of science. Thus these philosophers would object that Reichenbach's argument for vindicating induction is not based on the real goal of science. The dif-

[18] Barker (2), p. 68.   [19] Reichenbach (32), pp. 447–48.

ference, however, is not at all important here. We could characterize the concept of a practical limit in terms of the actual limit in something like the following way: φ is the practical limit of a sequence of events if, and only if, φ is the actual limit and is capable of being discovered within the area of human experience. Those who wish to insist that science seeks truth, not mere predictability, have only to understand the term "practical limit" in this sense. Those who wish to insist that science primarily seeks predictability have only to understand this term in the rendering more faithful to Reichenbach's presentation. Those who do not care may use either one. The fact is that, insofar as Reichenbach's entire argument is sound, it can be carried through using either of these constructions of the concept of a practical limit.

We come now to the way Reichenbach formulates the inductive method. The formulation he uses will have to be a rule for determining limits from the relative frequencies found in that portion of a sequence open to inspection. He states the rule of induction as follows:

If an initial section of n elements of a sequence x_i is given, resulting in the frequency f^n, and if, furthermore, nothing is known about the probability on the second level for the occurrence of a certain limit p, we posit that the frequency f^i $(i > n)$ will approach a limit p within $f^n \pm e$ when the sequence is continued.[20]

The condition that nothing be known concerning the probability on the second level prohibits the results of previous inductions from being taken into consideration in the use of this rule.[21] Thus posits are determined on the basis of observational data alone. At first blush, this may appear to be a shortcoming of this rule. Someone accustomed to using the term "induction" to refer to the various methods of argument employed in science to combine facts, hypotheses, laws, and even whole theories into complex inference patterns may object that this rule fails to reconstruct these methods of argument. But, rather than a failing, this is actually a virtue. Because this rule makes no use of results of previous inductions, it is free of any inductive assumption which would make the justificatory argument viciously circular by including such knowledge as a condition for its applica-

[20] Reichenbach (32), p. 446.

[21] Higher-level inductions are discussed by Reichenbach (30), pp. 363–73, and (32), pp. 311–33.

tion. Reichenbach introduced this restriction precisely in order to safeguard his argument against such circularity. He warned that, "if a great deal of knowledge is taken for granted, the inductive inference assumes particular forms that are justified only on the basis of tacit assumptions."[22] The rule ought not be construed as a reconstruction of complex theoretical inference patterns in science merely because such patterns are sometimes referred to by a term which is badly stretched to encompass them.

Having determined Reichenbach's construction of the end and means, we are now in a position to see how they are related in Reichenbach's vindicative argument. He begins by pointing out that the reason why no guaranty of the truth of inductive conclusions is possible is that such a guaranty would require an a priori assurance that, in fact, there are regularities. Thus Reichenbach makes it a cornerstone of his argument that nothing is known about the existence of sequences of events whose frequency of occurrence converges to a limit. The definition of the concept of the limit of an infinite series is such that a series $n_1, n_2, \ldots$, is characterized as having a limit if, and only if, there is a number p such that, however small we choose a positive number e, there is an n_i such that for every n_j, if $n_j > n_i$, the absolute difference between the relative frequency f^{n_i} and p is less than e. This means that, for the purpose of vindicating induction, we cannot presuppose knowledge of whether there is such a p for any sequence of events.[23]

But, from the fact that we have no knowledge of the existence of regularities, it does not follow that there are no regularities. As Reichenbach puts it:

We have no proof for the assumption [of the existence of a limit of the frequency]. But the absence of proof does not mean that *we know that there is no limit;* it means only that *we do not know whether there is a limit.* In that case we have as much reason to try a posit as in the case that the existence of a limit is known; for, if a limit of the frequency exists, we shall find it by the inductive method if only the acts of positing are con-

[22] Reichenbach (32), p. 431.

[23] Reichenbach sometimes formulates the limit assumption in terms of the possibility of prediction (e.g., see Reichenbach [30], pp. 350–51). I have omitted this construction of the limit assumption for the simple reason that I wish to present Reichenbach's position in the strongest form possible. The difficulty with this construction is that, though no limit exists in a certain sequence, it is, nevertheless, possible for someone accurately to predict the character of individual events (e.g., by luck).

tinued sufficiently. Inductive positing in the sense of a trial-and-error method is justified so long as it is not known that the attempt is hopeless, that there is no limit of the frequency. Should we have no success, the positing was useless; but why not take our chance?[24]

To forestall a possible misunderstanding of this last statement, Reichenbach adds:

> The phrase 'take a chance' is not meant here to state that there is a certain probability of success; it means only that there is a possibility of success in the sense that there is no proof that success is excluded.[25]

By way of supplementing what Reichenbach has said, we may add that the reason we cannot know there are no sequences which converge to a limit is the same as the reason we cannot know there are such sequences. This knowledge would also require the use of induction to establish it, and this is forbidden in constructing a justification.

But, as Reichenbach points out, this state of affairs does not preclude asking—and, perhaps, answering—the question, "What advantages would induction possess, relative to the non-inductive methods, if there were sequences in nature with limits?" For the sake of answering this question, Reichenbach tentatively assumes that there are sequences with limits. That this is only a tentative assumption and will eventually be eliminated is pledged by Reichenbach. "When we wish to overcome Hume's skepticism we must eliminate this last assumption from our justification of induction."[26] Given this assumption, then, in what respects are inductive posits better than ones based upon non-inductive rules?

To answer this, Reichenbach appeals to a feature of induction which has long been regarded as one of its chief merits—its self-correctiveness.[27] He argues:

> The inductive posit is not meant to be a final posit. We have the possibility of correcting a first posit, of replacing it by a new one when new observations have led to different results. From this point of view, the following analysis of the inductive procedure can be made. If the sequence has a limit of the frequency, there must exist an n such that from there on the frequency f^i $(i > n)$ will remain within the interval $f^n \pm e$, where e

---

[24] Reichenbach (32), p. 475.　　　　　　[25] *Ibid.*

[26] Reichenbach (32), p. 472.

[27] In this regard, note Salmon's correction of Black's argument that there is no guaranty that inductive revisions are truly corrections (Salmon [35], pp. 35–36).

is a quantity that we choose as small as we like, but that, once chosen, is kept constant. Now if we posit that the frequency f^i will remain within the interval $f^n \pm e$, and if we correct this posit for greater n by the same rule, we must finally come to the correct result. The inductive procedure, therefore, represents a *method of anticipation;* in applying the inductive rule we anticipate a result that for iterated procedure the limit must finally be reached in a finite number of steps.[28]

Succinctly, the argument is this: If there is a limit of the frequency in a sequence of events, then, if Reichenbach's rule is applied repeatedly and consistently, it will eventually give estimates of that limit to any preassigned degree of approximation.[29] In contrast to what is usually encountered in the writings of inductivists, this argument is remarkable because it can be established without the aid of an inductive premise. The truth of its conclusion rests solely upon logico-mathematical considerations.

To prove that this hypothetical is demonstrably true, it is sufficient to show that, assuming an arbitrary sequence of events possessing a limit and assuming that Reichenbach's rule is consistently used in iterative application, we can deduce that an estimate of the limit is ultimately discovered which is accurate to any desired degree of approximation. Let $c_1, c_2, \ldots,$ be the sequence with which the events in an arbitrarily chosen reference class C take place, and let P be a property which the members of C may exhibit. Let $f_1, f_2, \ldots,$ be the sequence of relative frequencies corresponding to the sequence of events $c_1, c_2, \ldots,$ such that each f_i expresses the relative frequency with which P has occurred in C through c_i. On the first assumption, that a limit of the relative frequency exists for P with respect to C, by the definition of the concept of a limit, we have

$$(e)(\exists N)(n) [(n > N) \supset (| f_n - p | < e)] , \qquad (1)$$

where e is a positive number, N and n are elements of $c_1, c_2, \ldots,$ and f_n is the relative frequency with which P occurs in C up through c_n. If now we choose as a value for e the positive number g (which is

[28] Reichenbach (32), pp. 445–46.

[29] The degree of approximation is, of course, made as small as we like by choosing the positive quantity e to be sufficiently small. However, the degree of approximation is *preassigned* in the sense that we regard e as chosen first because the definition of the limit concept says that, *for each choice of* e, *a suitable* N *can be found,* but N may be different for different choices of e.

selected because it is sufficiently small to give us an estimate which is as accurate an approximation as we desire), then (1) becomes

$$(\exists N)(n)[(n > N) \supset (|f_n - p| < g)] . \qquad (2)$$

If we take m to be the number, or one of the numbers, whose existence is guaranteed by (2), then we have

$$(n)[(n > m) \supset (|f_n - p| < g)] . \qquad (3)$$

Since $c_1, c_2, \ldots, c_m$ is finite, by our second assumption, that Reichenbach's rule is consistently used in iterative application to the sequence $c_1, c_2, \ldots$, it follows that this rule comes to be applied to the segments $(c_1, c_2, \ldots, c_{m+1}), (c_1, c_2, \ldots, c_{m+1}, c_{m+2}), \ldots, (c_1, c_2, \ldots, c_{m+1}, c_{m+2}, \ldots, c_{m+s}), \ldots$, thus producing the sequence of posits $f_{m+1}, f_{m+2}, \ldots, f_{m+s}, \ldots$. According to (3), however, each of these posits is within the interval $p \pm g$. This, then, proves that, if a limit exists and if Reichenbach's rule is continually applied, the limit must be ascertained by this rule within whatever is chosen as the desired degree of approximation.

Though this is true, and even demonstrably so, the proof requires, as we have just seen, the tentative assumption of the existence of a limit of the relative frequency. If this assumption can be dispensed with on satisfactory grounds, then Reichenbach will have established that induction's repeated positing of the persistence of the observed relative frequency must eventually yield estimates of a limit which are accurate within any desired degree of approximation and remain so. To show that this first assumption can be eliminated in his argument, he argues:

We used the assumption of the existence of a limit of the frequency in order to prove that, if no probabilities are known, the anticipative posit is the best posit because it leads to success in a finite number of steps. With respect to the individual act of positing, however, the limit assumption does not supply any sort of information. The posits may be wrong, and we can only say that if it turns out to be wrong we are willing to correct it and to try again. But if the limit assumption is dispensable for every individual posit, it can be omitted for the method of positing as a whole. The omission is required because we have no proof for the assumption. But the absence of proof does not mean that *we know there is no limit:* it means only that *we do not know whether there is a limit.* In that case we have as much reason to try a posit as in the case that the existence of a limit is known; for, if a limit of the frequency exists, we shall find it by the inductive method if only the acts of positing are continued sufficiently. Inductive positing in the sense of a trial-and-error method is justified so long as it is not known that the attempt is hopeless, that there is no limit of the frequency. Should we have no success, the positing was useless; but why not take our chances?[30]

Those acquainted with *Experience and Prediction* will recall Reichenbach's analogy of the fisherman:

> We may compare our situation to that of a man who wants to fish in an unexplored part of the sea. There is no one to tell him whether or not there are fish in this place. Shall he cast his net? Well, if he wants to fish in that place I should advise him to cast the net, to take the chance at least. It is preferable to try even in uncertainty than not to try and be certain of getting nothing.[31]

Reichenbach's point is that his argument does not try to establish induction as a knowledge claim but attempts only to justify acting in accord with induction. Thus the dispensability of this assumption is a consequence of what we are committed to when we profess the aim embodied in the chosen end. Though nothing can be known concerning the presence or absence of limits, since we profess the aim of discovering any existing limits, we are required to do everything in our power to reveal them. Thus, since there is a possibility that limits exist, we are committed to acting on that possibility because the alternative—no action at all—makes it certain that we will fail to achieve the end.[32] Hence, if induction is our best bet, the assumption

---

[30] Reichenbach (32), p. 473.   [31] Reichenbach (30), pp. 362–63.

[32] Thus, nothing ventured, nothing gained. But it might be argued that this maxim is simply an empirical truth discovered by inductive extrapolation from the experiences of ne'er-do-wells—hence, that Reichenbach's argument is circular at this point. For, it may be argued further, it is quite possible that venturing nothing will be a good method for gaining something in the future. After all, the world might be such that, if the fisherman merely does nothing, he would soon find fish jumping into his boat, whereas, if he casts his net, they would swim away. Likewise, the world might be such that, if we were to refrain from performing non-demonstrative inferences and conduct no experiments, true hypotheses would just pop into our heads like silly thoughts. This, however, does not constitute a serious objection to Reichenbach's argument, because, if we accept the assumption here—that inactivity is a form of activity which can lead to definite results—we must consider the maxim, "Nothing ven-

that there are limits is dispensable as a cognitive claim because fixing the vindicative end makes it no longer needed as a premiss.

We now come to the crux of the problem faced by Reichenbach. He states it in the following terms:

> So long as no probabilities have been established, the inductive rule cannot be based on theorems of the calculus of probability; therefore we cannot prove that the inductive rule leads to the posit of the greatest weight, nor do we know how probable it is that the limit posited will be reached. We cannot even prove that the posit becomes better with a greater number of observations. . . . In what sense, then, can the inductive posit be justified if we have no proof that the posit will lead to the greatest number of successes?[33]

Reichenbach answers this question by arguing that with induction we can make wagers which are as favorable to us as possible. He writes that ". . . the question of success is for us indeterminate, and we may therefore at least dare a wager. The wager, however, should not be arbitrarily laid but chosen as favorably as possible."[34] What Reichenbach will have to show, then, is that induction provides wagers that are either the most favorable to us or at least favorable enough.

How do we know that induction constitutes the best means, or at least an adequate one, for finding limits if there exist any? Reichenbach says:

> If there is a limit of the frequency, the use of the rule of induction will be a sufficient condition to find the limit to a desired degree of approximation. There may be other methods, but this one, at least, is sufficient. Consequently, when we do not know whether there is a limit, we can say, if there is any way to find a limit, the rule of induction will be such a way. It is, therefore, a necessary condition for the existence of a limit, and thus for the existence of a method to find it, that the aim be attainable by means of the rule of induction.[35]

This, however, does not mean, as some philosophers have mistakenly thought, that Reichenbach bases his choice of induction on the fact

---

tured, *something* gained," to be a method of discovering truths about the future. But, if we do this—consider it on a par with induction and its alternatives (palmistry, hunches, clairvoyance, and the like)—then it will turn out to be definitely inferior to induction in that it cannot be shown to be convergent, whereas induction can.

33 Reichenbach (32), pp. 444–45.   34 Reichenbach (30), p. 362.

35 Reichenbach (32), p. 474.

that it can be employed to assess any of its rival non-inductive rules. These philosophers are, of course, right in observing that this would not give us the epistemological warrant to say that Reichenbach's rule is preferable to those it is used to assess. Clearly, on pain of vicious circularity, there can be no reason for regarding such an order of assessment as the order of preference. Non-inductive rules might just as well be used to assess the validity of induction. But Reichenbach does not adopt this form of argument, though he does say that we ordinarily use induction to assess the merits of other predictive procedures and implies that, were we in possession of a justification of induction, the assessment we actually make would be epistemologically justified.[36] Both these things are true, but neither plays a role in Reichenbach's vindicative argument.

At this point, Reichenbach's argument gets into difficulty. Reichenbach has shown that inductive success is a necessary condition for the success of any rule. But, as we have shown in section 2.2, merely showing that a means is a necessary condition for attaining the end is no vindication. All methods may fail. However, Reichenbach also claims that induction is a sufficient condition for finding a limit. But, if we refer back to the proof, we see that induction is a sufficient condition only on the assumption that inductive positing continues past the number m. If m is so large that it cannot be passed by mortal scientists, then induction is not a sufficient condition for actually finding limits. Reichenbach cannot appeal to the notion of a practical limit here because he cannot by the same kind of argument prove that induction is a sufficient condition for finding practical limits. Let us assume the existence of practical limits. Then, by definition, there are sequences of events which reach sufficient convergence within the domain of human experience for mortal scientists to find their limits. But notice that this assumption is quite empty because it guarantees only that mortal scientists can find these practical limits by *some* method. It does not guarantee that they will find them with induction. All that follows from assuming the existence of practical limits is that there is at least one method of non-demonstrative inference which must succeed. This, however, is too weak to serve as a vindication of induction because the number m may be too large for induction but

[36] Black (3), pp. 168–79, has argued correctly that the use of induction to assess other methods proves nothing, but he mistakenly takes this to be part of Reichenbach's argument. Salmon (35), pp. 37–38, has criticized Black. But Reichenbach is quite explicit that this plays no role in his justificatory argument (see [30], pp. 353–54, and [32], pp. 475–76).

not for some non-inductive method. The assumption cannot be interpreted as asserting that m is sufficiently small to guarantee inductive success because, then, the argument would be merely assuming the success of inductive inference. This is enough to show that Reichenbach's argument so far breaks down as a vindication because establishing the expediency of the method is a necessary condition for establishing its preferability. For a preferability vindication is stronger because it shows not only that a method will work but that it works best.

Let us say that a method of positing has the property of convergence if, and only if, in terms of the foregoing proof it can be demonstrated that its persistent use with sequences possessing limits or practical limits must sooner or later give estimates of those limits, and these estimates become and remain accurate to whatever degree of approximation is chosen. Induction is, therefore, convergent. But, as we have just shown, this is not enough to warrant the claim that it is expedient or preferable. Not only might some other methods have this property, but we know of infinitely many that have it. This was the form in which Reichenbach was aware of the inconclusiveness of this phase of his argument. In fact, Reichenbach provides us with a very convenient characterization of the methods which share with induction the property of convergence:

The posit f^n is not the only form of the anticipative posit. We could also use a posit of the form $f^n + c_n$, where c_n is an arbitrary function, which is chosen such that it converges to 0 with n increasing to infinite values. All posits of this form will converge asymptotically toward the same value, though they will differ for small n.[37]

Thus the methods by which posits can be made divide into two classes which are jointly exhaustive: the convergent methods and the non-convergent methods. So far, what Reichenbach's argument shows is only that a convergent method is preferable to a non-convergent one. To establish a preference for induction over each of the other convergent methods, it will have to be shown, not only that its posits converge asymptotically toward the limit in a sequence and ultimately come and remain within a predetermined degree of approximation, but that it possesses some other property which gives it an advantage the others do not have. That this is indeed necessary can perhaps be illustrated best with the summary Reichenbach gives of his basic

[37] Reichenbach (32), p. 447.

argument, changed only by replacing all references to induction by X, where X may be any convergent rule whatever:

Every action depends on two presuppositions. The first is of a volitional nature: we wish to attain a certain aim. This aim can, at best, be reduced to more general volitional aims, but it cannot be given other than volitional grounds. . . . The second presupposition is of a cognitive nature: we must know what will happen under certain conditions in order to be able to judge whether they are adequate for the attainment of the aim. . . . Only the combination of the two presuppositions, the volitional aim and the knowledge about the future, makes positive action possible. . . . The first presupposition need not be discussed here. Within the boundaries of a logical analysis we investigate the second presupposition for action, that is, the cognitive presupposition. Now it is clear that, though the X rule does not supply knowledge of a future event, it supplies a sufficient reason for action: we are justified in dealing with the anticipative posit as true, not because we can expect success in the individual case, but because if we can ever act successfully we can do so by following the directive of X. The justification of X constructed may, therefore, be called a *pragmatic* justification: it demonstrates the usefulness of the X procedure for the purpose of acting. It shows that our actions need not depend on a proof that the sequence under consideration have the limit property. Actions can be made in the sense of trials and it is sufficient to have a method that will lead to successful trials if success is attainable at all. It is true that this method has no guarantee of success. But who would dare to ask for such a guarantee in the face of the uncertainty of all human planning? . . . If we cannot base our actions on demonstrative truth, we shall welcome it that we can at least take our chance.[38]

Thus the entire argument so far goes through for every convergent method. We cannot accept it for one and not accept it for all, and we cannot accept it for all because they are mutually incompatible. Therefore, we cannot accept it for induction, and this means that we require some extension of the argument which shows that induction is preferable to each of the competing convergent rules.

Since Reichenbach's formulation of induction has come to be known as "the straight rule," let us, by analogy, call the other convergent rules "crooked rules." A crooked rule is, then, a rule which, given an initial segment of a sequence of events C consisting of n elements of which r have the property P, yields the value $(r/n) + c_n$ as the estimate of the limit of the frequency of P in C, where c_n is any function which converges to zero as n approaches infinity except the

[38] This is taken, with the indicated change, from (32), pp. 480–81.

constant function 0. The rule which produces as our wagers values of the function r/n—the rule which posits the persistence of the observed relative frequency—is thus the straight rule. Since there are infinitely many functions c_n bound by the condition that their values converge to 0 as n goes to infinity, there are infinitely many crooked rules. Thus we may state the problem Reichenbach tried to solve as the problem of grounding a preference for the straight rule over each of the infinitely many crooked rules.

Reichenbach offered two "solutions" for this problem. The first appears in his book *Experience and Prediction*. This proposal is subsequently abandoned in favor of the second, which appears in the more recent statement of his position contained in *The Theory of Probability*. The first is this:

> The "correction" c_n may be determined in such a way that the resulting wager furnishes even at an early stage of the series a good approximation of the limit p. . . . On the other hand, it may happen also that c_n is badly determined, i.e., that the convergence is delayed by the correction. If the term c_n is arbitrarily formulated, we know nothing about the two possibilities. The value $c_n = 0$—i.e., the inductive principle—is therefore the value of the smallest risk; any other determination may worsen the convergence. This is a practical reason for preferring the inductive principle.[39]

Although Reichenbach does not tell us the reasons why he abandoned this argument, they are not hard to guess. If the statements "any other determination may worsen the convergence" and "the value $c_n = 0$ . . . is therefore the value of the smallest risk" are taken to mean that there is a chance, simply a possibility, that induction delays the convergence least, then this holds for each non-inductive rule too. Relative to some particular crooked rules, the straight rule may possibly yield characteristically slower convergence. This interpretation thus offers nothing that might establish a preference for the straight rule. But, if this is not what is meant by such statements, then they must be interpreted to mean that there is a greater probability that the crooked rules worsen the convergence. How, then, we may ask, is such a probability established? To establish that with the straight rule the probability of early convergence is higher than with any crooked rule, we would have to know at what N's the straight rule achieves convergence for various types of sequences and at what N's each of the crooked rules achieves convergence for the

---

[39] Reichenbach (30), p. 355.

same cases. But, without any appeal to experience and without using any rule of non-demonstrative inference, we can have no idea of what such N's might be, and so we cannot determine such a probability. We cannot make use of factual knowledge to project beyond what has been observed because we cannot here use the inductive method. We cannot instead use a crooked rule because, judged by it, the straight rule would appear to be the rule which slows convergence. We cannot use any of the usual statistical assumptions concerning frequency distributions. We cannot even try out a few rules and see for ourselves because we have no way to project what we see to what it is reasonable to expect to see in the future. Without at least one of these items, no purely mathematical theorems from the calculus of probability can help. Consequently, we cannot use this interpretation to establish a preference for the straight rule. Therefore, we need no longer guess why Reichenbach abandoned this line of argument; there is no way to show that induction embodies the least risk without begging the question, or even worse.

The second "solution" Reichenbach offers is this:

We cannot prove the rule of induction to be superior to other methods included in this class. There may be, and in general will be, forms of the function c_n that are more advantageous than the function $c_n = 0$. If we knew one of these forms, we should prefer it to the rule of induction. The method of correction . . . may be regarded as an instrument for finding such forms. When, on the contrary, we know nothing, we can choose what we like. The rule of induction has the advantage of being easier to handle, owing to its descriptive simplicity. Since we are considering a choice among methods all of which will lead to the aim, we may let considerations of a technical nature determine our choice.[40]

In the only other place where we find this argument, Reichenbach says: "We shall prefer the inductive posit f^n, for which $c_n = 0$. To do this we can, however, adduce only grounds of descriptive simplicity; that is, the inductive posit is simpler to handle."[41] In order to understand what is involved in this new turn of Reichenbach's argument, we must inquire into his discussion of descriptive and inductive simplicity.

Reichenbach distinguishes between these two kinds of simplicity on the grounds that descriptive simplicity is a psychologistic concept, while inductive simplicity is an epistemological one. Descriptive sim-

[40] Reichenbach (32), pp. 475–76. [41] *Ibid.*

plicity has to do with the ease with whch human investigators are able to handle a construction. We prefer the construction which is descriptively simpler for reasons of "taste," "convenience," or "economy." As an example of what he means, Reichenbach cites the way ease in computation determines our choice of the metric system over the system of yards and inches.[42] According to Reichenbach, descriptive simplicity has nothing to do with truth, "for this kind of simplicity . . . concerns only the description and not the facts co-ordinated to the description."[43] Descriptive simplicity, as a criterion, applies only in cases where two or more constructions are logically equivalent in terms of their empirical content. Conversely, inductive simplicity applies only in cases where two or more constructions are logically non-equivalent with respect to certain of their as yet-unverified consequences. Thus inductive simplicity is relevant to the choice between various hypotheses or theories when they are equally well supported by the available evidence and when some of their unverified consequences are inconsistent with those of the others. In the case of inductive simplicity, Reichenbach denies that our preference for the simpler construction is based upon economy of handling, convenience, or taste:

Actually in cases of inductive simplicity it is not economy which determines our choice. The regulative principle of the construction of scientific theories is the postuate of the best predictive character; all our decisions as to the choice between unequivalent theories are determined by this postulate. If in such cases the question of simplicity plays a certain role for our decision, it is because we make the assumption that the simplest theory furnishes the best predictions. This assumption cannot be justified by convenience; it has a truth-character and demands a justification within the theory of probability and induction.[44]

Unfortunately, his account of descriptive and inductive simplicity together with his claim that the straight rule is preferable on the basis of descriptive simplicity place Reichenbach in an impossible situation: the choice between the straight rule and the crooked rules cannot be made in terms of descriptive simplicity or inductive simplicity. By definition, the criterion of descriptive simplicity applies only to constructions which are logically equivalent; and the various members of the class of convergent rules are incompatible with each

[42] Reichenbach (30), p. 374.   [43] *Ibid.*

[44] Reichenbach (30), p. 376.

other, since, before convergence takes place, each gives different posits from each of the others. But, on the other hand, the choice between the straight rule and the crooked rules cannot be made on the basis of inductive simplicity either. As this notion has been defined, the criterion of inductive simplicity makes its selection of the simplest construction on an inductive assumption to the effect that the simplest construction is the best predictor. Because this assumption has a truth character, Reichenbach insists it itself must be justified within the theory of probability and induction. Thus, were he to base his preference for the straight rule on inductive simplicity, he would commit a *petitio principii.*

Reichenbach was, we must suppose, unaware of this difficulty with his importation of simplicity. And he said nothing more about the justification of induction than what we have reported in the preceding discussion.

Lenz has criticized Reichenbach in the following way: "Reichenbach does mention simplicity as a ground for choosing the straight rule, but this is surely a very weak ground and is, in any case, separate from his 'pragmatic justification.' "[45] Lenz concludes his criticism of Reichenbach by saying that Reichenbach has "too many rules of induction from which to choose and no apparent grounds upon which to make a choice."[46] However, as we have seen, simplicity is by no means separate from Reichenbach's argument but plays a crucial role in it. Lenz finds no apparent grounds on which Reichenbach can make a choice only because he does not recognize the grounds on which Reichenbach does choose. Lenz's remark that simplicity is a very weak ground is not only at variance with the proved importance of simplicity considerations in inductive projection[47] but, here, begs

[45] Lenz (21), p. 4. Lenz makes another too hasty criticism of Reichenbach. He argues that Reichenbach "correctly saw that predictions made on the basis of any of these rules [the convergent rules] converge toward the actual limit eventually, that is, as the evidence gets larger and larger; but what he failed to appreciate is that, before this happens, the predictions we make vary tremendously depending upon which rule is used." Lenz is, as we have seen, quite wrong. Reichenbach was fully aware that, before convergence, posits obtained from a crooked rule can vary greatly from inductive posits. This is why he first sought to show that the straight rule runs the least risk of slowing the convergence and then sought to show that its posits are preferable because it is descriptively simpler.

[46] *Ibid.*

[47] There is an overabundance of examples, but Goodman (13), pp. 63–120, and Kemeny (19), pp. 391–408, will do.

the very question at issue. Whether or not simplicity can serve as a basis for preferring the straight rule to all the crooked rules is just the question to be decided. True enough, Reichenbach's own construction of simplicity turns out, on analysis, to be unsatisfactory; but Lenz does not even give it the benefit of the analysis. Reichenbach's mistake was simply to offer an unsatisfactory way of meeting his difficulties, but he did not err in neglecting to propose a relevant way in which they might be met.

This puts us in the following position. The mere fact that Reichenbach's own attempt to establish a preference for the straight rule over the crooked rules is inadequate does not condemn the vindicative argument to which it is appended. Nor does it follow that a different attempt of the same kind will fail also. Some extension of Reichenbach's argument may exist which would overcome the problem peculiar to his supplementation and offer a genuinely satisfactory basis for preferring induction. Should such an extension be found, induction would be justified. Therefore, it is our task to demonstrate that no such extension exists, and to do so in a way which shows that every argument for justifying induction is, like Reichenbach's argument, inconclusive and without the possibility of such extension.

3.5. This argument of Reichenbach's is the special case for our reduction. But there are certain considerations which raise the question whether it is not too special a case. Reichenbach, as we have seen in the previous section, adopts what is called the "frequency interpretation" of the concept of probability and formulates induction in these terms. Thus Reichenbach's rule says that, if we observe an initial segment of a sequence consisting of n elements in which the relative frequency for the occurrence of a certain property is r/n, we are to posit that the limit of the relative frequency will be within $(r/n) \pm e$ when the sequence is extended without bound. To evade certain well-known difficulties with the frequency theory,[48] the more modern frequency theorist would formulate induction differently. For example, as the rule that if we observe the frequency r/n of a fixed event E for a large n of random experiments performed under constant conditions, we are to posit that, in a long series of repetitions of such experiments, the frequency of E is approximately equal to r/n (or, if the series were infinitely continued, the frequency of E would

[48] These are discussed, among other places, in Nagel (23).

approach some definite ideal value very near r/n).[49] But such differences within the frequency-theory position do not require corresponding changes in Reichenbach's justificatory argument because such rules as the immediately preceding are obviously convergent and are obviously counterpoised by essentially the same class of crooked rules.[50] Thus Reichenbach's argument is not too special a case in the sense that it cannot be accommodated into a non-Reichenbachian variant of the frequency theory. However, there is a non-frequency interpretation of the concept of probability, the so-called *logical* interpretation, where the differences are such as might be taken to imply that Reichenbach's argument is too special a case. In this section we shall show that these differences are not such that our special case is too specialized.

According to the logical interpretation of the concept of probability, a probability value expresses the degree of evidential support (weight, degree of confirmation, etc.) conferred on a statement by a set of evidence statements, the degree being determined by the particular logical relation between the confirmed statement and the statements which confirm it. To illustrate the difference between the frequency and the logical interpretations of the notion of probability, let us consider the following two sets of examples of probability statements:

(1) (*a*) The probability that a man marries his mother-in-law is 0.000000002.
   (*b*) A legacy of a million dollars is less probable than one of fifty dollars.
   (*c*) The probability that a normal die will come up 6 is one in six.
   (*d*) It is highly probable that someone exposed to a virus while in a weak condition will catch it.
(2) (*a*) The degree to which Snell's law is confirmed by the evidence is 0.98.
   (*b*) Given present evidence, the theory of combustion is far more probable than the phlogiston theory.
   (*c*) It is extremely unlikely that Pythagoras' refusal to eat beans altered the course of ancient philosophy.

[49] Cf. Cramér (8).

[50] A crooked version is obtained in a straightforward manner. If the frequency r/n of a fixed event E for a large n of random experiments performed under constant conditions is observed, then posit that in a long series of repetitions of such experiments the frequency of E is approximately equal to $r/n + c_n$, where c_n is a function of n bound to the condition that, as n goes to infinity, the values of c_n go to zero.

(*d*) Relative to the evidence now available, your hypothesis has more factual support than it did relative to the evidence when you first proposed it.

The concept of probability involved in (1) is the frequency concept. Thus these statements are interpreted as asserting that the relative frequency with which the type of event they concern occurs in the specified reference class approaches such-and-such a value as a limit with increasing n. What this means exactly may be seen in the following terms: If a sample containing n members is selected from the reference class, and from this sample we compute the number r of elements which are instances of P, we obtain the relative frequency with which the members of the sample are cases of P which is r/n. If we enlarge this sample by including further members of the reference class, then enlarge it again, and continue enlarging it again and again without bound, each time determining the relative frequency with which P occurs in the new sample, we obtain an infinite sequence of relative frequencies which corresponds to the sequence with which the events in the reference class occur. In general, the ratios in the sequence of relative frequencies will be different for different-sized samples; that is, as the size of the sample changes, the ratios also change. But what is asserted by statements asserting that the occurrence of P approaches a limit with increasing n is that the change in these ratios is such that, after the sample reaches a certain finite size, they cluster about some fixed value φ in such a way that they differ from φ by an exceedingly small positive quantity which decreases asymptotically as the sample becomes greater and greater.

Therefore, every probability statement to which the frequency interpretation applies is an empirical statement. Such statements make assertions about the world whose truth or falsity must be determined on the basis of observation and experimentation, though such a determination is never fully conclusive.[51] But the statements to which the logical interpretation applies—the statements in (2), for example—are non-empirical. They assert a logical relation (analogous to deducibility) between a hypothesis and its evidence statements expressing the degree to which the truth of the former is entailed by the truth of the latter statements. Thus the truth or falsity of such probability statements is solely a matter of whether or not the probability value expresses the actual confirmation relation between the statements in-

[51] Cf. Nagel (23), pp. 394–95.

70

volved. The question of verification is, therefore, one which can be settled by purely logical considerations.

This is the fundamental difference between these two interpretations of the concept of probability. There are other differences, however. For example, statements involving the frequency concept are statements about kinds of events, whereas statements involving the logical concept often concern particular events. But there are similarities too. Both are construed as functions of two variables whose values range between 0 and 1; both are objective notions of probability; both satisfy certain axioms in the mathematical theory of probability; and both are important in science.

Systems of probability logic are constructed to provide the rules in accord with which this logical relation can be determined for arbitrary pairs of a hypothesis and evidence statements and can be employed to assign a probability value to the hypothesis. Because the rules of such a system determine both the types of confirmation relation and the specific probability values to be assigned in the case of each type, they suffice to establish the truth or falsity of probability statements when under the interpretation provided by such a system. This does not mean that we will accept the interpretation of a particular probability logic without first considering whether the method by which it assigns probability values determines degree of evidential support in a satisfactory manner. Some probability logics might confer probability values in such a way that hypotheses we cherish turn out to be very weakly supported, while those we regard as ridiculous turn out to be very highly confirmed.

What we shall show is that there is a spectrum of probability logics as wide as the spectrum of convergent rules and that the choice between the convergent rules has its analogue in the choice between such logics. To show in this way that our special case is not too narrow, it will be necessary to examine one such system in some detail. Because Carnap's system of inductive logic is the most elaborate and popular of any of those so far proposed, we shall use it as our example.[52]

Carnap's theory deals with an infinite sequence of finite languages L_N (and an infinite language L_∞, which we shall not concern ourselves with here). These languages are forms of lower functional logic

[52] Though the most comprehensive statement of Carnap's theory is to be found in (6) and (7), we shall take our discussion in the following pages from his convenient summary in (5).

with identity—certain applied functional calculi. Relative to these languages, "atomic sentence" is defined as a sentence consisting of a predicate of degree n with n individual constants. The conjunction of all atomic sentences in a language L_N is called a "state-description" because, relative to the predicates in L_N, it describes a possible state in the domain of individuals. Replacing some of the conjuncts by their denials gives another state-description. Thus the class of all state-descriptions in L_N consists of all the conjunctions which may be obtained in this manner, including the original one. There are to be semantical rules for each L_N which determine, for each sentence j and each state-description i which can be formulated in L_N, whether j holds in i (i.e., whether j would be true if i describes the actual state in the domain of individuals). The "range of j in L_N" is, then, the class of state-descriptions in L_N where j holds. With respect to the concept of range, Carnap defines the basic notions of deductive logic. A sentence which holds in every state-description (i.e., whose range is universal) is logically true. A sentence whose range is null is logically false. A sentence which holds in some but not every state-description is synthetic in the sense that factual information about the real state of affairs in the domain of individuals is necessary to determine its truth. Two sentences with the same range are logically equivalent. If there are two sentences, say, e and h, where the range of e is wholly included in the range of h, then e logically implies h.

Carnap's inductive logic is developed upon this deductive basis by the introduction of the concept of degree of confirmation. This introduction involves three steps: first, the definition of the notion of a regular c-function; then, the definition of the notion of a symmetrical c-function; and, finally, the definition of the notion of degree of confirmation, c^*.

A statement in Carnap's inductive logic of the form "$c(h, e) = p/q$" is a statement about the degree to which the range of e (to be thought of as the evidence statement or conjunction of evidence statements) is included in the range of h (to be thought of as the hypothesis). To be able to express the degree of inclusion in numerical terms, Carnap constructs a metric for ranges, an "m-function" as he calls it. Since any m-function will lead to a particular c-function which enables us to express how much of the range of e is a part of h, once Carnap has chosen such a metric, he is in a position to measure degree of inclusion. According to Carnap:

A numerical function m ascribing real numbers of the interval 0 to 1 to the sentences of a finite language L_N is called a regular m-function if it is constructed according to the following rules:

(1) We assign to the state-descriptions in L_N as values of m any positive real number whose sum is 1.

(2) For every other sentence j in L_N, the value of $m(j)$ is determined as follows:

    (a) If j is not L-false, $m(j)$ is the sum of the m-values of those state-descriptions which belong to the range of j.

    (b) If j is L-false and hence its range is null, $m(j) = 0$.[53]

Given any regular m-function, Carnap defines its corresponding c-function as follows:

(3) For any pair of sentences e, h in L_N, where e is not L-false, $c(h, e) = m(e \cdot h)/m(e)$.[54]

Just for purposes of completeness, let us note how Carnap defines an m-function for the infinite language L_∞ and its corresponding c-function. Thus, in those instances where the specified limit exists,

(6) $m(j)$ in L_∞ is the limit of the values $m(j)$ in L_N for $N \to \infty$.

(7) $c(h, e)$ in L_∞ is the limit of the values $c(h, e)$ in L_N for $N \to \infty$.[55]

It is not difficult to see that among those theorems which are based upon this definition of a regular c-function will be many of the main theorems of the theory of probability, including, for example, Bayes's theorem and the multiplication theorem.

The next step consists of narrowing down the class of regular c-functions to a class containing only symmetrical c-functions, thus limiting the choice of a particular function to express degree of confirmation to this less comprehensive class. Carnap's rationale for this particular step is the desire to make his inductive logic general in the same respect in which deductive logic is general, that is, no discrimination is made among individuals. The class of symmetrical c-functions is, thus, just those regular c-functions which treat all individuals on a par with respect to the determination of $c(h, e)$. Carnap writes:

Two state-descriptions in a language L_N are said to be *isomorphic* or to have the same structure if one is formed from the other by replacements of the following kind: we take any one-one relation R such that both its domain and its converse domain is the class of all individual constants in

---

[53] Carnap (5), p. 74.   [54] *Ibid.*   [55] Carnap (5), p. 75.

L_N, and then replace every individual constant in the given state-description by the one correlated with it by R. If a regular m-function (for L_N) assigns to any two isomorphic state-descriptions (in L_N) equal values, it is called a *symmetrical* m-function; and a c-function based upon such an m-function in the way explained earlier is then called a *symmetrical* c-*function*.[56]

The last step in constructing a definition of degree of confirmation is to choose one particular symmetrical c-function $c*$ as the explicatum for this notion. Carnap first defines a concept he calls a "structure-description":

Let i be a state-description in L_N. Suppose there are n_i state-descriptions in L_N isomorphic to i (including i itself), say i, i', i'', etc. These n_i state-descriptions exhibit one and the same structure of the universe of L_N with respect to all the properties and relations designated by the prdicates in L_N. . . . This common structure of the isomorphic state-descriptions i, i', i'', etc., can be described by their disjunction i v i' v i'' v. . . . Therefore, we call this disjunction, say j, a *structure-description* in L_N.[57]

Since the range of j contains only the isomorphic state-descriptions i, i', i'', etc., according to $(2)(a)$, $m(j)$ is the sum of the m-values for these state-descriptions. Given that m is symmetrical, these values are equal. Thus

(I) $m(j) = n_i = m(i)$.[58]

And, conversely, if m (j) is known to be q, then

(II) $m(i) = m(i') = m(i'') = \ldots = q/n_i$.[59]

Thus this final step amounts to fixing the distribution of m-values for the structure-descriptions in L_N. Carnap gives each of the structure-descriptions equal m-values. This choice determines a particular m-function $m*$ and a particular c-function $c*$ based upon $m*$ in the manner of $(1)-(3)$ above. Hence we have

(III) (a) $m*$ is a symmetrical m-function;

  (b) $m*$ has the same value for all structure-descriptions (in L_N).[60]
Since each state-description belongs to the range of exactly one structure-description, by (I) the sum of the $m*$-values for all structure-descriptions is equal to the sum of the $m*$-values for all state-

---

[56] Carnap (5), p. 79.   [57] *Ibid.*   [58] Carnap (5), p. 80.

[59] *Ibid.*   [60] *Ibid.*

descriptions is equal to 1. Consequently, if the number of structure-descriptions in L_N is m, then, by (III)(b),

(IV) For every structure-description j in L_N, $m^*(j) = 1/m$.[61]

According to (III)(a) and (II), we have

(V) $m^*(i) = 1/mn_i$,

where i is any state-description in L_N and n_i is the number of state-descriptions isomorphic to i.[62] On the basis of this definition of m^* as applied to state-descriptions, Carnap defines m^* as applied to sentences of L_N in analogy to (2) (a)(b).[63] If a sentence is not logically false, its m^*-value is the sum of those state-descriptions which belong to its range; if it is logically false, its m^*-value is 0. Finally, c^* is defined on the basis of the previous definition of m^* so as to conform to (3); for any pair of sentences e and h in L_N, where e is not L-false, $c^*(h, e)$ is taken as the quotient $m^*(e, h)$ over $m^*(e)$.[64]

This is the core of Carnap's system of inductive logic. Let us now show that interpreting probability statements in accord with this system does not provide a means of circumventing the problem of induction. In the first place, even if no form of the problem of induction could arise in the context of an inductive logic, this would not mean that we have an escape from the problem. The frequency theory applies to statements which involve event types, whereas degree of confirmation applies to statements which are about particular events or which are hypotheses or theories.[65] Thus there is no possibility of interpreting the problem away, for at best we use a probability logic to localize the problem in the area of statements of the former kind. But, the problem of induction arises in the context of inductive logic, too.

The class of symmetrical c-functions is infinite. Any two arbitrarily chosen members of this class can be expected to determine very different values as the degree of confirmation for the same evidence statements and the same hypothesis. Thus the particular form the problem of induction assumes in this context is the question of what justification there is for choosing a certain c-function to determine degree of confirmation instead of any of the other possibilities? Carnap, who was concerned only with the task of explication, justified

---

[61] *Ibid.*   [62] *Ibid.*   [63] *Ibid.*

[64] Carnap (5), pp. 80–81.

[65] This was noted at the beginning of this section.

his decision to adopt c^* instead of c_w, the alternative choice proposed by Wittgenstein in the *Tractatus*,[66] on the basis of inductive knowledge. Wittgenstein's proposal is based on the apparently reasonable supposition that a priori there is no reason to take one state-description as more probable than another, and so it assigns equal m-values to all state-descriptions. Carnap easily shows that "the choice of c_w as the degree of confirmation would be tantamount to the principle never to let our past experience influence our expectations for the future."[67] "This," Carnap concludes, "would obviously be in striking contradiction to the basic principle of all inductive reasoning."[68] But the matter is not so easily settled here. The implication is that this suffices as a *reductio* of Wittengstein's proposal and thus serves as a partial justification of c^*. This implication is warranted for Carnap, who can presuppose "the basic principle of all inductive reasoning," but not for anyone who wishes to justify induction. Such a person has to find some other way to show that his choice of a c-function is preferable. The fact that c_w is incompatible with c^* is no condemnation of either. There is a problem precisely because the various c-functions are mutually incompatible.

The range of possible c-functions is, moreover, the same as the range of convergent rules, for each has an analogue in the other type. Perhaps the easiest way to show this is simply to take Carnap's formula $c^*(h, e) = m^*(e, h)/m^*(e)$ as the counterpart of the straight rule and modify it by adding for each crooked rule its "correction" function. We shall not even try to discuss the analogue of the convergence proof in inductive logic because this topic is fraught with difficulties. For one thing, it would be reasonable to say that the analogue of this proof would be a proof that the degree of confirmation of a true hypothesis approaches 1 (or, perhaps, that it ultimately transcends and stays above a certain fixed level) as the number of its positive instances increases without bound; but, at least in Carnap's system, the degree of confirmation of any universal hypothesis is always 0. One may rephrase in terms of instance confirmation, but this, too, has grave difficulties.[69] But, fortunately, there is no need to discuss this. That the case we have chosen for the reduction is not too specialized is shown clearly by the fact that both frequency theo-

[66] Wittgenstein (39), propositions 4.4, 4.26, 5.101, and 5.15.

[67] Carnap (5), p. 81. [68] *Ibid.*

[69] For a discussion of the difficulties see Putnam (27).

ries and probability logics choose from essentially the same body of rules.

3.6. In this the final section we shall complete the reduction. The first step toward completion is a generalization of the problem left by Reichenbach.

It is often claimed that the problem of induction cannot be independent of the task of explicating induction because, first, we must know exactly what it is we are trying to justify. This claim is partly correct and partly incorrect. It is partly correct in that the rule we choose to justify or show unjustifiable may be unjustifiable for reasons that are peculiar to it alone. Had our explication gone a little further, perhaps we might have found a formulation which can be justified. Perhaps a rule which, at present, we consider non-inductive is, in fact, better than the ones we consider inductive, so that what prevents a justification is simply the inadequacy of the too hastily chosen justificandum. All this can be easily granted. In fact, we can take this line of argument a step further. Perhaps we are radically, not merely slightly, wrong about which rule ought to be the justificandum. Perhaps some very highly non-inductive rule, some seemingly quite bizarre crooked rule, is capable of being justified while no other convergent rule is. Even this can be granted. Nothing we have admitted shows an essential incompleteness of skeptical arguments. Rather, it shows that the problem left by Reichenbach needs to be generalized. If, instead of constructing the problem as one of vindicating the straight rule, we construct it as a problem of vindicating any one of the convergent rules, this generalization enables us to avoid such incompleteness. Thus this claim is partly wrong in that it asserts that independence from the task of explication can be achieved only by a fully satisfactory explication. Independence can also be achieved by this generalization of the problem.

However, such a generalization will serve its purpose only if the body of rules involved is exhaustive. Thus the second step toward completing the reduction is to show that the class of convergent rules contains all the alternatives which need to be considered. Here Reichenbach helps us out. He divided all methods for predicting and generalizing from something known to something unknown into two classes. The first is the class of those methods for which there is an explicit formulation in terms of a rule with a c_n which converges to zero with increasing n ($c_n = 0$ in the case of induction), and the second is the class of those methods which lack an explicit formulation in terms of a rule.[70] The methods which can be explicitly stated as rules but are not convergent are omitted because they are clearly less adequate than those which are convergent. The methods which, though they are claimed by their adherents to be sound predictors, have never been codified as rules are such methods as clairvoyance, crystal ball-gazing, various forms of extrasensory perception, palmistry, dreams, intuitions both of the male and female variety, tea leaves, etc. Reichenbach argues that there is no way to know whether such methods produce posits which ultimately converge upon the limit.[71] This is surely so. Because, for them, there is no rule to tell us how they work, we cannot give a demonstration that with them perseverance, if only it perseveres, must eventually pay off, as it must in the case of the convergent rules.[72] Reichenbach concludes that it is preferable to use induction (and we may add any crooked rule, for that matter) to using one of these methods. But there is an even stronger reason for not considering them to be real alternatives. There being no formulation of the procedure by which they determine posits, they cannot even be shown to be alternatives. How do we know that they are not inductive? Described simply as clairvoyance, palmistry, reading tea leaves, etc., we cannot be sure that the method represents anything over and above a skilful use of induction. This reflection leads to the realization that we are doubly safe in regarding the class of convergent rules as exhaustive. If one of these methods is explicitly formulated in terms of a rule, it will be either convergent or not. If it is not convergent, we have the best of grounds for dismissing it. If it is convergent, it will be equivalent to one of the rules in the class of convergent rules. For the criterion of equivalence is surely the extensional one; whether both rules make the same posits in the same situations, and given that for every unique function c_n there is a unique convergent rule, there is a convergent rule for every unique system of mappings of data sets onto posits.

To make our argument for exhaustiveness complete, we should explicitly include inductive and crooked rules for projecting lawful hypotheses as well as statistical ones. Thus we shall take it as understood that the class of convergent rules includes such rules. In the next chapter we shall consider certain examples of these rules and show in what sense they are convergent and how the crooked rules

[70] Reichenbach (32), pp. 475–76. [71] Reichenbach (32), p. 476.

[72] This point applies to Black's Lord High Forecaster (see Black [3], pp. 177–79).

for this type of projection are formed. Hence we are now in the position to formulate the special case.

Reichenbach's argument, though inconclusive, does delimit the problem to a choice between convergent rules. Thus the problem becomes whether Reichenbach's argument can be extended to show that some convergent rule is expedient or preferable to all the others. This, then, is the sense in which Reichenbach's argument is a special case whose positive solution is a necessary condition for a positive solution to the general problem. Let us call this problem "the problem of the convergent rules," or simply "PCR." We may formulate it as follows: *Show either that one convergent rule is preferable or expedient to use to arrive at the best assumption about unknown events or that no such vindication is possible.* It should be emphasized, perhaps, that using Reichenbach's argument as the test case does not make our solution depend on any aspect of his argument except such considerations as are involved in the convergence proof. His argument is taken only as an example embodying the essential characteristics of a vindicative argument for induction. We shall treat it as representative in this sense, so that our solution applies to each and every argument of the relevant form. The choice of Reichenbach's argument was dictated primarily because it is the most carefully worked out convergence argument—and nearly the only one —and secondarily because it is the most widely known vindicative argument.

With the possibility of a validation eliminated on Humean grounds, the general problem is thereby reduced to one of vindicating a policy of action in accord with one of the convergent rules. The net effect of Reichenbach's argument is to show why the alternatives for a vindication are limited to methods which guarantee convergence. Therefore, taken as the special case, Reichenbach's argument amounts only to a program. The problem of the convergent rules, the problem which stands in the way of a satisfactory completion of this program, shows that, besides what has already been demonstrated, another factor, at least, must enter the picture. This new factor is, as Reichenbach was himself aware, a criterion of simplicity, though, naturally, not a criterion of descriptive simplicity after his suggestion.

CHAPTER FOUR

The Solution of the Problem

4.1. The point which caused us to generalize the problem left by Reichenbach in the form of the problem of the convergent rules (PCR)—that one of the crooked rules might prove to be justifiable while the straight rule might be unjustifiable—is not merely academic. There is a sense in which the straight rule is, in fact, less satisfactory than one of the crooked rules. Suppose we toss a coin 1,000 times and get 497 heads. For such a sample the straight rule posits that the relative frequency of heads is equal to the observed relative frequency 497/1,000. This posit, however, is somewhat counterintuitive, since, ordinarily, we simplify and take $\frac{1}{2}$ to be the best posit. There are crooked rules whose c_n function automatically simplifies in the ordinary way so that these c_n functions yield the value 3/1,000 for $n = 1,000$, which makes the estimate $\frac{1}{2}$ as desired. One such rule, which, as it were, has a simplifying device built in, would thus appear to stand a better chance of being justified than the straight rule. Alternatively, one might say that such a rule has a better claim to the rubric "inductive" than does the straight rule because its results correspond more closely to what we regard as good scientific posits. Either way, it is clear that the choice to formulate the problem abstractly was a good one. Moreover, it is clear that the c_n functions must be viewed as the mathematical embodiment of simplicity criteria, though, admittedly, bizarre ones in many cases. Reichenbach saw them as varying the inductive theme in more complex harmonic schemes. It would appear better, rather, to say that the theme undergoes both more complex and more simple variations.[1]

Kemeny makes a point very closely related to this. Since his discussion of this and the other points taken up in his important paper, "The Use of Simplicity in Induction," sheds light on matters with which we are directly concerned, it will be worthwhile examining

[1] The difficulty discussed in this paragraph was first seen by Russell (34), p. 370.

them in some detail.[2] Kemeny begins by offering a partial explication of the concept of simplicity, insofar as it applies to two standard types of inductive problems. The first type is the classical urn problem. This serves as his paradigm for the case of determining the relative frequency with which a certain event occurs in a particular reference class. The problem is to find the ratio of white balls to black balls on the basis of n draws, m of which are white. The second type is the problem of curve-fitting. This serves as his paradigm for the case of determining lawful hypotheses. Here the problem is to select a polynomial which correctly describes the functional relationship between two independently measurable quantities, given n measurements each of which expresses the value of one of the variables for a preassigned value of the other.

The first rule Kemeny considers, "Select a hypothesis which is as well in agreement with the observed values as possible," is, in effect, Reichenbach's straight rule, though formulated differently.[3] The use of this rule presupposes a criterion of agreement for which Kemeny introduces a measure of the deviation. In the urn case this measure is the absolute value of the difference between the observed relative frequency and the predicted relative frequency, whereas in the curve-fitting case it is the average of the absolute differences between observed and predicted values. In the urn case this rule requires us to choose, if possible, a posit such that the deviation is zero, that is, the observed value is equal to the predicted value. Thus this rule is definitely Reichenbach's straight rule here. But, in the curve-fitting case, there is a certain indeterminacy owing to the fact that a deviation of zero can be secured in infinitely many ways. For such a deviation all that is required is that the curve pass through each of the observed values, and this requirement can be satisfied by infinitely many curves, each with a different form of oscillation between the observed values. As a consequence, Kemeny's rule is a schema for infinitely many rules, only one of which is Reichenbach's. Kemeny complains that this first rule does not guarantee convergence. Each of the rules for which this schema stands is convergent, but, because the schema allows us to switch from one to the other by any method whatever, prediction is not fixed by any particular rule. To remedy this, Kemeny introduces a new rule which is simply the expected modification: "Select a hypothesis which is as well in agreement with the observed values as possible; if there is any choice left, choose the

[2] Kemeny (19).   [3] Kemeny (19), p. 394.

simplest possible hypothesis."[4] This rule can be taken as the correlate of Reichenbach's rule for the case of curve-fitting.

Kemeny next considers the chances of choosing the true hypothesis by this rule, and he finds that, though it is ideally suited to obtain very accurate approximations of the true hypothesis, the chances of actually obtaining the true hypothesis decrease to zero with increasing n. In the urn case this is due to the fact that the predicted value changes each time n changes, whereas in the curve-fitting case it is due to the fact that the probability that all our measurements are correct decreases as the number of measurements made increases. This leads Kemeny to reject this rule also.

In its place he proposes the following rule: "Select the simplest hypothesis compatible with the observed values. (If there are several, select any one of them.)"[5] This rule has none of the difficulties of its predecessors, and Kemeny considers it to be a satisfactory reconstruction of what scientists actually do. But there are two key terms which are in need of explication—"simplest" and "compatible." We shall not follow Kemeny in his explication of the latter term, because it is of no direct interest. It is sufficient to report that, according to his results, a hypothesis is compatible with a certain body of data if these data do not make the hypothesis too improbable in terms of some suitably chosen level of deviation.[6] We now turn our attention to what is said about the concept of simplicity.

To begin with, since the standard of compatibility underdetermines the choice of a hypothesis, simplicity considerations must make a unique selection from among those remaining. What, then, are the features of a hypothesis (here ratios and polynomials) by virtue of which one is simpler than another? What is the structure of the criterion which employs these features to decide? These are deep questions, and Kemeny does not try to provide anything like a complete answer. He starts with certain intuitively obvious cases; for example, $\frac{1}{2}$ is simpler than $503/1,000$ and $1/3$ is simpler than $331/1,000$. According to Kemeny, in such cases simplicity lies in the fact that simpler ratios can be expressed by smaller numbers. Moreover, it is intuitively obvious that we cannot choose $1/3$ as simpler than $2/3$, first, "because they occupy symmetric positions"; second, because "$2/3$ white balls is the same as $1/3$ black balls"; and, third, because

---

[4] Kemeny (19), p. 396.

[5] Kemeny (19), p. 397.   [6] Kemeny (19), p. 398.

"these two fractions would hardly ever be both compatible with the same observations."[7] Kemeny thus concludes that

at least in the urn example we can safely state that simplicity consists in the smallness of the denominator of r. Of course it could be objected that the same fraction can be stated in an infinity of forms, but if we take advantage of this supposed difficulty, then we get a deeper insight into the simplicity ordering. Let us divide all fractions into classes, the kth class having all fractions with denominators $\leq 2^k$, $k = 0, 1, 2, \ldots$ Then there are few duplications within a given class, and each new class contains all the previous ones $(1/3 = 2/6 = 3/9,$ etc.$)$. Thus we see that allowing greater complexity (less simplicity) coincides with allowing ourselves more freedom of description and greater accuracy. Hence we note that rule 3 can also be stated as a warning: do not use more precision in your theories than is necessary to explain the observations.[8]

In the case of selecting a polynomial, Kemeny finds that simplicity consists in the smallness of the exponent primarily and in the smallness of the coefficient secondarily. Choosing the simplest hypothesis is choosing the polynomial with the lowest exponent, unless there is more than one, in which case the simplest polynomial is the one whose coefficient size is smallest (as determined by some test such as the size of the largest denominator in the coefficients). Finally, for the case of finite decimal expansions, he says, "we order them according to the number of decimal places. Each new class contains the previous ones, since we can always put 0's at the end of the decimal expansions. Then, e.g., if we measure $.1234 \pm .005$, we must select $.12.$"[9] Thus, "the rule tells you to use no more digits in your summing up of results than is necessary to be within the experimental error."[10]

Kemeny next offers a justification to show that his improved rule gives us a satisfactory chance of choosing the true hypothesis. We must examine his argument carefully to see if he succeeds where Reichenbach failed. But it should be made quite clear that, though Kemeny himself is concerned exclusively with the problem of explication, we are treating his argument as if it were intended as a justificatory argument. For there is no prima facie reason why it might not be used as a justificatory argument.

There are, according to Kemeny, only two reasons why the hypothesis chosen by this rule might be false: (i) the true hypothesis might

[7] Kemeny (19), p. 399.   [9] *Ibid.*

[8] *Ibid.*   [10] *Ibid.*

be incompatible with the evidence, so that the rule selects from among a set of hypotheses each of which is false, or (ii) the true hypothesis might be compatible with the evidence, and yet there might be a simpler hypothesis which is also compatible with it.[11] As he points out, however, reason (i) poses only a negligible danger because the standard of compatability can be chosen so as to provide overwhelming odds against the possibility that the true hypothesis is incompatible with the evidence. Thus, showing that his rule yields the best chance of selecting the true hypothesis requires him to show why he can rely on it despite the possibility that it may fail to choose the true hypothesis because a simpler one is also in agreement with the evidence.

Kemeny's argument is, basically, a more precise version of the one first proposed by Reichenbach for his concept of inductive simplicity.[12] According to Kemeny, since we are assured that the true hypothesis is compatible with the evidence, we can make it as much of a certainty as we like that the rule selects the true hypothesis. He argues as follows:

As we know from statistics, as n increases, the deviations allowed by the compatibility requirement decrease. Hence for high n we can find an interval around the observed values (an interval that can be made as small as required by increasing n) such that all compatible hypotheses lie within this interval. This, of course, is not enough; this only assures convergence under rule 3. But *the characteristic property of orderings according to simplicity* is that for any given hypothesis, even though there may be finitely many hypotheses at least as simple, we can find an interval within which there is no other hypothesis as simple (or simpler). Hence, by making n large enough we can make the interval of compatibility sufficiently small so that if the true hypothesis lies within it, no other hypothesis as simple will be in it. Hence for all sufficiently high n we must select h if it is compatible with the observations. Hence for all sufficiently high n we are 99 per cent sure of selecting h. *This is the justification we offer....*[13]

And, regarding the relation of his work to Reichenbach's, Kemeny says:

He [Reichenbach] believes that any choice of c_n is as good as any other, and hence he sets $c_n \equiv 0$, on grounds of "descriptive simplicity." Our posit, the simplest fraction compatible with m/n, can also be thought

11 Kemeny (19), p. 400.

12 Reichenbach (30), pp. 373–87.   13 Kemeny (19), p. 400.

of as a choice of a function c_n (since the interval of compatibility tends to 0, the difference between our posit and Reichenbach's must also tend to 0), only c depends not only on n, but also on m. Hence we argue that Reichenbach is quite right in saying that the posit must be of the form $m/n + c_n$, but we argue that there is one choice of c_n superior to others (since it gives us not only convergence but an excellent chance of finding the true hypothesis), and that it is not the choice of $c_n \equiv 0$.[14]

Kemeny's claim is that, in fact, one of the crooked rules is preferable to the straight rule. But, besides being further evidence that the problem must be formulated abstractly, this argument makes it appear as if we now have a true justification of induction. However, appearances are, in this case, deceptive.

Let us begin by looking at the final step in Kemeny's explication of simplicity—the conditions he lays down for an ordering of hypotheses according to simplicity. He states:

Hypotheses are *ordered according to simplicity* if we have the following four conditions satisfied:

Condition 1. The hypotheses are divided into sets $H_{(a, \ldots, z)}$, where a, . . . , z are natural numbers (called the *characteristic numbers*). These sets are ordered lexicographically according to the characteristic numbers. (The hypotheses in earlier sets being called simpler than the ones occurring only in later sets.)

Condition 2. The later sets include the earlier sets in the following sense: $H_{(a, \ldots, k, \ldots, z)}$ is always a subset of $H_{(a, \ldots, k+1, \ldots, z)}$.

Condition 3. For every set H there is an integer N_H such that, if a member of H is compatible with e^n ("e^n" designates the actual outcome of the n experiments) for some $n \geqq N_H$, then no member of H or of any earlier set can be compatible with this e^n.

Condition 4. N_H should in each case be as low as possible. (Or better, each h_i ("h_i" designates one of the hypotheses we choose from) should belong to a set H with an N_H as low as possible.)[15]

One thing to bear in mind concerning these conditions is that, in a very significant sense, they are quite empty. That is to say, they in no way prescribe what actual features of hypotheses or differences between hypotheses count in assigning hypotheses to different sets in the ordering. If we have a choice between a linear function and a quadratic one, though intuitively we would say that the former is simpler, these conditions, by themselves, do not determine its selection. Of

[14] Kemeny (19), pp. 406–7.   [15] Kemeny (19), p. 403.

course, the considerations adduced by Kemeny previously are meant to provide such a basis for determining class membership, but these considerations are independent of these conditions in the sense that they may be used in connection with considerations which are contrary to Kemeny's.

Taken as a justificatory argument for induction, Kemeny's argument is inconclusive and cannot offer a basis either for preferring his rule or for establishing its usefulness by an expediency vindication. Kemeny's rule—"Select the simplest hypothesis compatible with the observed values. (If there are several, select any one of them.)"—can be modified similarly to the way in which the straight rule was in generating the crooked rules. Stripped of its honorific connotations, "simplicity" signifies, in this connection, one particular way of assigning hypotheses to sets ordered in a sequence according to preferability. Thus, by a method of assignment according to simplicity, hypotheses assigned to a set s_i are preferable to those assigned to s_j if, and only if, s_i occurs in the sequence earlier than s_j. We may think of the other methods of assignment as specific permutations upon this one which assigns a hypothesis to a set in such a way that simpler hypotheses are assigned to earlier, higher preference, sets. To differentiate among these different methods of assigning hypotheses to sets in a sequence ordered according to preferability, let us introduce such terms as "zimplicity," "yimplicity," "ximplicity," . . . , "simplicity," . . . , etc. We now have sets of conditions, formally the same as Kemeny's, for ordering according to zimplicity, ximplicity, yimplicity, and so forth. These orderings allow us to formulate rules parallel to Kemeny's; for example, "Select the zimplest hypothesis compatible with the data, and, if there are several, then select any one of them." Such rules will have, like Kemeny's, a formulation in terms of a c_n function.[16] Thus there is multiplicity where there first seemed only simplicity.

The easiest way to establish the inconclusiveness of Kemeny's argument is to show that it can be used to justify such alternative rules. To show this we need merely replace the terms "simplicity," "simpler," and "simple" in Kemeny's argument by the terms "zimplicity," "zimpler," and "zimple," since, then, the result is a justification of the rule to select the zimplest hypothesis. But not both

16 For such rules, c_n is chosen so as to depend upon m as well as upon n, but to depend upon m and n in such a way as to favor zimple rather than simple hypotheses.

Kemeny's argument and the one which results from such replacement can be sound because then every rule is justified.

To see what has gone wrong, let us compare these two arguments. First, both rules are convergent so that, insofar as the argument depends upon convergence, there is no difference. Second, neither rule can be criticized in the way Kemeny criticized Reichenbach's rule because both are formulated so that, if a hypothesis is once chosen, it is not subsequently abandoned unless it becomes incompatible with the evidence or unless some /simpler/zimpler/ hypothesis becomes compatible with the evidence. Hence in neither case do our chances of selecting the true hypothesis progressively deteriorate, becoming vanishingly small with increasing n, as in the case of Reichenbach's straight rule. Thus the only aspect left which affords a comparison which can account for the fact that not all rules can be equally good is the number of observations necessary in the two cases to find the true hypothesis or a satisfactory approximation of it, whichever we decide to seek.

There are, then, three possibilities: in general, one of the two rules will require a smaller n in order to be successful; in general, both require the same $n;$ in general, both rules require an n which is too large to be attained by science. The last of these possibilities can be dismissed because we can proceed on the assumption that one of these rules is capable of success. If no rule works, we can forget about the whole business; if there is some rule which works, we may assume that it is one of these. Given this assumption, if the second possibility is the case, and we can prove that it is, we have an expediency vindication of both rules; while if the first is the case, and we can prove that it is, we have a preference vindication of the rule which requires the smaller n. But Kemeny's attempt to show that his rule does not require n's that are too large depends on an assumption that the laws of nature are sufficiently simple;[17] and, presumably, he would argue also that his rule requires, in general, smaller n's than does the zimplicity rule because the laws of nature are more simple than zimple. But, because the assumption about the simplicity of the regularities in nature is inadmissible in the context of an attempt to justify induction (we could just as well contend these laws are more

[17] Kemeny asks, "Couldn't the 'sufficiently large n' be too large for practical purposes?" In reply he says, "How high this n is depends, of course, on how simple the true hypothesis is." And then in a footnote to this sentence, "This is the point at which an assumption about the 'Simplicity of Nature' can come in" (see Kemeny [19], p. 402).

zimple than simple), interpreted as vindicative argument, Kemeny's argument is inconclusive. In the next section we will see why this must be so.

4.2. This section presents the proof that PCR is essentially unsolvable, which, given the soundness of our reduction, is a proof that there can be no justification of induction. But, before this proof can be rigorously formulated, it will be necessary to formulate certain definitions and conventions.

The proof we shall present will have to apply both to the projection of lawful hypotheses and to the projection of statistical hypotheses. Thus this proof will have to be developed with respect to two types of cases. The two types we will employ will be essentially the same types as those Kemeny worked with in his study of simplicity. The case of statistical projection is the problem of predicting the ratio of members of a certain reference class C having the property P, given that we have a sample containing n members of C of which r possess P. The case of lawful projection is the problem of selecting a polynomial to express the manner in which a certain dependent variable behaves as a function of a certain independent variable, given that we have a finite set of observed values containing n elements.

But, before we describe these cases more fully, it should be pointed out that not every inductive problem in science belongs to one of these types. Nevertheless, they are the types of problem most commonly met with and are fundamental to the use of inductive procedures in science. Furthermore, we shall use these types as paradigmatic for all cases of statistical and lawful projection, so that the application of the proof to other cases will turn out completely trivial. Hence developing the proof in terms of these two types of cases does not impose a limitation upon the scope of its results.

Case I.—Here we wish to choose a hypothesis about the relative frequency of members of C having the property P on the basis of a knowledge of the frequency with which P occurs in a sample S drawn randomly from C. S consists of n members of C of which r possess the property P. In terms of our knowledge that r/n of the members of S are P and that S is randomly chosen from the superset C, we are to select a hypothesis to express the actual relative frequency of P's in C or to express a sufficiently accurate approximation of this relative frequency. The hypotheses in this case are, therefore, definite numbers Q, where Q is any rational number between 0 and 1. Examples of Case I include such instances as the problem of discovering the ratio of males with brown eyes in the population and the problem of determining the probability of contracting lung cancer after twenty years of smoking.

Case II.—Here we wish to choose a hypothesis to describe the relationship existing between two independently measurable quantities on the basis of a sample S consisting of n tests in which we have determined for certain values of the independent variable x the associated values for the dependent variable y. S thus contains n-ordered pairs of values which express how y varies for the n values of x considered. If we assume that the functional relationship can be expressed by some polynomial with rational coefficients and exponents, the problem in this type of case is to choose one such polynomial to describe the functional dependency either in such a way that, given an arbitrary value of x, we can predict exactly the associated value of y or in such a way that, given an arbitrary value of x, we can predict the associated value of y within a certain preassigned interval. Examples of Case II include such instances as the problem of determining the way the pressure of a gas varies as a function of changes in its temperature and the problem of finding the rate at which certain materials decay radioactively.

The next matter to take up is the alternative preference orderings for hypotheses based upon alternative assignment systems. In the last section we found that, besides the ordering according to simplicity which figured in Kemeny's argument, there were also orderings according to zimplicity, yimplicity, ximplicity, etc., which resulted from different methods of assigning hypotheses to sets ordered in a sequence according to preferability. Let us refer to such orderings as "orderings according to complexity" and distinguish among particular orderings by employing the symbol O with different subscript letters to indicate different individual orderings. As we pointed out in the preceeding section, each O other than O_s, the ordering according to simplicity, may be regarded as simply a different shuffling of the complexity ranking established by O_s; but, conversely, O_s may be regarded as simply a unique shuffling of some other O. Collectively, the orderings according to complexity constitute the entire spectrum of possible preference scales, each particular ordering being based upon a different notion of how complexity and preferability are to be related. Thus we may have one ordering which takes fractions with one thousand places in their denominators as preferable to ones with more or less places, one which takes polynomials with such fractions in their exponents as preferable to polynomials with higher or lower exponents, one which takes fractions and exponents which are prime as preferable to ones which are not, etc.

The convergent rules for both types of case will be of two kinds: there will be rules designed primarily to select hypotheses which provide estimates of the true regularities within any desired degree of approximation and there will be rules designed primarily to select the true hypothesis. For cases of Type I, the rules of the former kind will take the form of instructions to posit $r/n + c_n$ as the relative frequency of P in C when r/n members of S are P. For this case the rules of the latter kind will take the form of Kemeny's third rule. They will be instructions to select the preferable hypothesis (according to a certain O) compatible with the data, the choice being arbitrary if there is more than one such hypothesis. For cases of Type II, the rules of the former kind, the approximation rules, may be constructed in various ways. Perhaps the most straightforward way to construct the convergent rules here is to choose a standard interpolation formula (e.g., Newton's or Lagrange's) as the counterpart of the straight rule and then to modify it by successively adding different functions which have the effect of transforming the polynomial interpolated by the unmodified version of the formula by adding a c_n as an additional term, where, again, the values of c_n decrease to zero as n goes to infinity. In this way the crooked rules are produced for this case. Moreover, such rules will be convergent in the desired sense because, given any pre-assigned interval of deviation about the true curve, the condition on c_n that its values diminish to zero with increasing n assures us that there is an N such that for all n's greater than N the interpolations remain within this interval of permitted deviation. Thus, each of these rules, if used persistently, will eventually give estimates of the true curve which are and remain precise to any predetermined degree of accuracy. The same thing applies to the analogue of the practical limit, the "practical curve."[18]

For Case II, the rules designed to select the true hypothesis will take the form of instructions to select the preferable polynomial or curve (according to a certain O) compatible with the evidence— again, the choice being arbitrary if there is more than one such

---

[18] The notion of a practical curve is simply that of a curve whose form can be determined in the range of human experience.

hypothesis. The analogue of the Kemeny rule here is one which interpolates the simplest curve connecting the observed points, and the analogue of those based upon other orderings according to complexity are rules which interpolate curves that oscillate in a certain characteristic way between the observed points. But these rules must eventually reveal the true curve, for, as more and more values of y are determined, more and more possibilities become incompatible with the evidence, and, thus, because the true hypothesis is in a position in each ordering which is a finite distance from the preferred choice for $n = 0$, the true hypothesis becomes the preferred one by some n.

We require that the rules of both kinds in each case be constructed in such a way that each rule unequivocally determines exactly one choice of a hypothesis for every sample. The justification for this condition is straightforward. If a rule fails to determine at least one hypothesis, it fails to serve its purpose; while, if it determines more than one hypothesis, it is inadequate because it projects hypotheses that are inconsistent in their predictions for certain cases. Hence, if a rule is to be fully adequate, it must provide a unique choice. But it may be asked whether an otherwise satisfactory rule can always do this. For example, does the intuitively most appealing rule R_s in which the favored hypothesis is the simplest of those conforming to the evidence uniquely determine a single hypothesis in every conceivable instance? Suppose we know that, in a certain case of Type II, the experimental results yield data points each of which falls on a line making a $45°$ angle to the x-axis and that the actual curve cannot continue in exactly the path taken so far. Quite obviously, under these circumstances there are not one but two distinct "simplest" curves, regardless of what was taken as the criterion for saying that one curve is simpler than another.

But there are no compelling reasons why we should demand that a rule refrain from making some arbitrary decisions, and there is no reason why we should demand that a rule make systematically congruous choices where there are no such choices to be made. If the rule R_s chooses a curve with a slightly upward slope of a certain curvature, there is, then, no reason why the existence of a curve with a slight downward slope whose curvature is the same should be taken as a criticism of R_s. The fact that there is no distinction between these two curves and yet there is a choice between them only goes to show that sometimes we must make choices without a systematic basis. It is presumably such cases of symmetry as this one which led Kemeny to formulate his rule with a stipulation for arbitrary choices. Thus each rule is to be considered so constructed as to select the hypothesis ranking lowest on its complexity ordering if there is a single lowest-ranking hypothesis. If not, it is constructed to select one of the lowest-ranking hypotheses arbitrarily. Should this hypothesis be subsequently eliminated, the rule makes further arbitrary choices, but all lowest-ranking hypotheses must be eliminated before the rule selects one ranking next lowest.

The rules from which PCR requires us to make a justified choice thus divide two ways. First, there are, in both Cases I and II, rules designed to provide good approximations to the true regularity and rules designed to select the true hypothesis itself. It would be a mistake if, like Kemeny, we were to dismiss the approximation rules as not corresponding to the procedures scientists use. Scientists are often compelled to settle for less than the exact truth. Consequently, statistical methods of approximation are widely employed in science, where it is utopian to demand the exact truth and nothing but the exact truth. We will sometimes not distinguish between these two types of rules, and for this purpose we make the following definition: A rule R_i is *successful* when and only when either R_i selects the true hypothesis or R_i provides estimates of the true regularity that are accurate, and will always remain accurate, to the preassigned degree of approximation.

Second, there are rules for cases of Type I and rules for cases of Type II, rules for projecting statistical hypotheses and rules for projecting lawful hypotheses. It will be convenient for us to neglect this difference and treat corresponding rules in each type of case together. Thus let us imagine that the rules for cases of Type I are paired with their counterparts in the rules for cases of Type II in terms of a correspondence which pairs rules having the same c_n function or rules having the same ordering according to complexity. Such pairs may themselves be considered as single rules.

We may now ask what the difference is between different rules. Given n observations, n outcomes, or n-ordered pairs of values, any two different rules R_i and R_j will yield predictions which correspond for each of these n observations, but they will differ in their predictions for cases that are not yet determined. Often, of course, a pair of different rules will not give different predictions for every unknown case. For any pair of rules R_i and R_j, we can expect that there will be some samples drawn from some populations such that, for some unknown cases, R_i and R_j offer the same predictions; but this correspondence is merely a similarity between different rules. If, for every sample S and every unknown case in the population from which S was drawn, R_i and R_j make exactly the same predictions, then R_i and R_j are just alternative formulations of the same rule. Thus different rules differ only in how they predictively characterize unknown cases. The difference between the way in which two rules characterize the unknown cases which they characterize differently is the only difference between them as different methods of non-demonstrative inference. But, looking at the formulation of the convergent rules, it is quite obvious that what determines this difference in predictive characterization of unknown cases is the ordering according to complexity or the c_n function which is built into a rule. If this difference in formulation were obliterated, the rules would all be the same. Hence we have a reformulation of PCR: *Show that a particular type of complexity, as represented either in the form of an ordering according to complexity or in the form of a* c_n *function, is preferable or expedient to use to arrive at the best assumption about unknown events or that no such vindication is possible.*

In terms of success, then, what difference is there between using one rule or another, between choosing to favor one type of complexity rather than another? Since we assume the existence of practical limits and practical curves and since all the rules are convergent, the only difference possible is a difference in the number of observations necessary for success. For, if for every C each rule were successful on the basis of the same number of observations, then all rules would be equivalent. Thus we have the following condition:

(C1) The difference between any two rules R_i and R_j in terms of achieving success is a difference with respect to the number of observations necessary for success in each case; and the difference between success and failure in the use of any rule is the difference between whether the number of observations necessary is too large to be obtained or whether it is sufficiently small.

Clearly, then, if a rule R_i is to be shown preferable to a rule R_j, then R_i must be shown preferable in terms of the way it differs from R_j. Thus, by C1, R_i must require fewer observations to be successful, since the only effect of using one rule rather than another is the difference in the number of observations necessary to reach convergence or to discover the true hypothesis. Likewise, if a rule R_i is to be shown expedient while R_j is not, then R_i must be shown to not need more observations to be successful than it is possible for mortal scientists to collect. Thus it is evident that one of the properties 'succeeds sufficiently early' or 'succeeds earliest' must be shown to be possessed by some R_i in order that PCR be solved. One of these two properties is, therefore, what, besides the property of finite attainability, must be shown to be possessed by a method of non-demonstrative inference if the problem of induction is to be solved positively.

But, before we can state this as a condition, the notions of sufficiently early success and earliest success must be unambiguously formulated. If there were but one sequence of events in the world, the meaning of these notions would be quite unambiguous. Let the symbol "sse" be the predicate "succeeds sufficiently early" and let the symbol "se" be the predicate "succeeds earliest." Then, given that there is only one sequence of events, the formula "sse (R_i)" says that R_i requires an N for success that is not too large to be obtained, and the formula "se (R_i)" says that R_i requires an N which is smaller than the N required by any other rule. However, since there are indefinitely many sequences of events in the world, it becomes necessary to say something further to make these formulas read unambiguously. The existence of a plurality of sequences opens the possibility that there is no one rule which yields success first in each and every sequence and no one rule which yields sufficiently early success in each and every sequence. It also opens the possibility that there may be great diversity in the performance of the same rule when applied to different sequences so that a comparison of the performance of different rules, when applied to the same body of sequences, cannot be made directly. Thus a further specification of the meaning of the notions *sufficiently early success* and *earliest success* is required to cover such cases. The natural extension for these cases is to take the rule that yields earliest success in the greatest percentage of all sequences as the one which offers earliest success and to take the rules that yield sufficiently early success in a high enough percentage of cases as the ones which offer sufficiently early success. But such a method fails to take account of the fact that earlier successes have greater utility than later ones. We want some scheme of weightings in terms of the size of N required for success with a particular rule such that success with $N = 1$ receives the greatest weight, success with $N = 2$ is weighted slightly less, success with $N = 3$ is weighted even less, and the weightings become proportionately smaller decreasing to zero as N increases without bound. There will be numerous alternative systems of this kind, but we need not concern ourselves with which particular system of weighting would be best. It suffices for our purposes to assume the adequacy of one such system. In terms of it we can specify the meaning of *earliest success* and *sufficiently early success* in an unambiguous way. Since such a weighting system treats each sequence in the same way, we may take earliest success to coincide with highest average score and sufficiently early success to coincide with sufficiently high average score.[19]

It is interesting to notice that the assumption of practical limits and curves is now built into the notion of success at the earliest or at a sufficiently early point by virtue of the fact that eventually the N's become so large that the weighting received for success at these N's is small enough to be not worth considering.

Now we may state the next condition:

(C2) To be adequate as a solution to PCR, a vindicative argument must establish either that some rule yields earliest success or that some rule yields sufficiently early success.

Given the way in which earliest success and sufficiently early success are characterized, there is an immediate corollary to (C2):

Let R_i be the convergent rule for which the vindicative argument is offered, then:

(C3) A necessary condition for satisfying (C2) is that there is at least one sequence of events such that the N at which the rule R_i achieves earliest success or sufficiently early success with this sequence be known.

This requirement that the N at which R_i first obtains the true law or an adequate approximation of it (which never afterward becomes inadequate) may be taken in the broadest sense such that it is satisfied not only by a knowledge of N but also by a well-substantiated estimate of N or by a knowledge of relationships between this N and others, that is, by a knowledge of a function of the form $N = f(N_1, N_2, \ldots , N_m)$. This qualification actually adds nothing to the statement of (C3), since either a well-substantiated estimate of N for a

---

[19] The notion of sufficiently early success may be considered somewhat vague because there is no exact specification of a number or upper limit which provides a cutoff point determining when success is sufficiently early and when it is too late. Any finite N whatever may be used. The argument requires that some N be chosen but does not require any particular one.

certain sequence or a knowledge of a function of this kind both pre-suppose that in some sequences we know the N at which suitable convergence or the discovery of the true regularity takes place. And such knowledge is all that is needed to satisfy (C3) in the first place. (Of course, a knowledge of the actual regularity in some sequences or a well-substantiated estimate thereof would suffice also, but this is clearly ruled out by the character of the problem [see (C5) below].)

We come now to the most important conditions for the proof that PCR is unsolvable and that no vindication of a convergent rule is possible. The crux of them is, informally, that, in order to know the N at which the rule R_i first achieves success with a particular sequence of events, it is necessary to know the complexity of the actual regularity in that sequence of events. Thus:

(C4.1) Given a rule R_i for approximating regularities (either limits or curves), and given a preassigned e which fixes an interval of permitted deviation about the true regularity, for a sequence of events whose general term is c_k, the N at which R_i first obtains successful convergence cannot be known without knowing the actual regularity of c_k (the true limit or curve).

(C4.2) Given a rule R_i for finding the true regularity (either limits or curves) for a sequence of events whose general term is c_k, the N at which R_i first obtains the true hypothesis cannot be known without knowing the true regularity of c_k (the true limit or curve).

Two things may be assumed for the proofs of both (C4.1) and (C4.2). First, in the case of approximating the actual regularity and in the case of finding it, we may assume an arbitrarily selected sequence of events c_k. Second, we may assume that the elements constituting the sample from c_k on the basis of which R_i is to extrapolate is randomly chosen and perfectly representative. This latter assumption does not materially affect our proofs. It merely permits us to treat N as if it were independent of the order with which the events in the sequence c_k come up. We are safe in making this assumption because, if this order had to be known to enable us to know N, there would *ipso facto* be no possibility of vindicating any convergent rule.

Let us take the proof of (C4.1) first. N is a function of e, since, as a rule, as e tends to 0, $N(e)$ increases beyond all bounds. But we may assume a choice of e, say, g, which may be any finite value, regardless of how large or small, so long as this choice is predetermined. Since the sequence of events c_k converges to the limit ϕ, the absolute value of the posited estimate of R_i minus the actual limit ϕ is greater than

g for only a finite number of terms of the sequence, that is, N terms. Likewise, if R_i is a rule for approximating curves, the posited estimates of R_i are outside the interval of permitted deviation for only a finite N. Hence, given $|R_i(c_k) - \phi| > g$ for only finite N, if we know either N or the desired approximation of ϕ, we know the other; and, without knowing one, we cannot know the other (for, relative to our assumptions, N and the desired estimate of ϕ are functions only of each other). Hence, knowing ϕ is necessary to knowing the N at which R_i first achieves successful convergence.

The proof of (C4.2) is as follows. The N at which R_i first selects the true hypothesis is simply the number of elements of the sequence c_k it is necessary to consider in order that every hypothesis rated preferable to the true one on the basis of the ordering according to complexity built into R_i is eliminated as incompatible with the evidence. (We can assume that, once selected, the true hypothesis is not subsequently abandoned, since this is only to assume the absence of spurious observations which would lead us to reject the true hypothesis.) Thus, for R_i, the true hypothesis is only a finite number of hypotheses away from the hypothesis that R_i rates first choice on one observation. However, the size of N will depend upon the character of the sequence of observations we make. Let h_1 be the hypothesis which R_i selects for the first observation, and let $h_2, h_3, \ldots, h_m$ ($m \gtrless 0$) be the sequence of hypotheses which come before the true hypothesis, h_{m+1}, on the basis of R_i's ordering according to complexity. Clearly, if we make our observations so that the next one is chosen because $h_1, h_2, \ldots, h_m$ all give the same prediction for it but h_{m+1} gives a different prediction, then it will take only this observation for R_i to obtain success; and, if we make our observations so that each observation of the next hundred is such that $h_1, h_2, \ldots, h_m, h_{m+1}$ all give the same predictions for it, then it will take over a hundred observations for R_i to obtain success. But, within the framework of the problem of induction, we cannot have any conception of what strategy for making observations in the case of c_k will lead to choosing the true hypothesis with the smallest actual number of observations. At best, we can pick each new observation so that only one of the two 'simplest hypotheses', the first and second choice as determined by the ordering according to complexity built into R_i, can survive confrontation with this observational datum. Thus we suppose that each observation is chosen so that the predictions of the two most preferable hypotheses conflict for it. (This is not strictly true, since we could just as well take the hypotheses in R_i's preference ranking in triplets, quadruplets, or quintuplets as in pairs. Even taking them in orders such as pairs, then triplets, then pairs, then quadruplets, then pairs, then quintuplets, and so on, is not excluded. But such complications can be ignored because the same argument as we shall give for the case of pairwise selection can be given for such cases.) But, now, if it is known that h_{m+1} is the true hypothesis, we know that N at which R_i first selects h_{m+1} because, again taking the hypotheses that are preferable to h_{m+1} according to R_i's complexity preference ordering to be $h_1, h_2, \ldots, h_m$, this N is simply $m/2$ if m is even and $m/2 + 1$ if m is odd. (That cases other than pairwise selection can legitimately be ignored can be shown by an example. Take selection in terms of triplets. If we know that h_{m+1} is the true hypothesis, then, here too, we know the N at which R_i first selects h_{m+1} because this N is simply $m/3$ if m is divisible by 3 and $m/3 + 1$ if m is not. Some non-pairwise cases can be quite complicated, but this is immaterial to the point at issue here.) Correspondingly, if we do not know that h_{m+1} is the true hypothesis, then we cannot know the N at which R_i first succeeds with the sequence c_k. Because the number of hypotheses which is compatible with any set of observations is always infinite and there is no way to determine which hypotheses must be eliminated before R_i selects the true hypothesis, there is no way to determine the number of observations required in order to refute all hypotheses R_i ranks preferable to the true one.

The final condition is merely an explicit statement of what has always been required of a justification of induction, viz., that it not beg the question.

(C5) No justificatory argument proposed as a solution to PCR can be satisfactory if it depends on knowledge of empirical laws; in particular, if it requires we know either limits or curves expressing functional relations between empirical variables.

With these conditions, it is now quite easy to prove the unsolvability of PCR. PCR is unsolvable if there is neither a preference vindication nor an expediency vindication of some convergent rule. By (C1) and (C2), establishing a justification of the former type amounts to showing that some rule yields earliest success, and establishing a justification of the latter type amounts to showing that some rule yields sufficiently early success. (C3) makes it a necessary condition on a justification of either type that it determine the N at which the rule to be justified first succeeds in some sequence of events. (C4.1) and

(C4.2) show that a knowledge of this N requires a knowledge of the actual limit or curve. Finally, (C5) enables us to conclude that PCR is unsolvable, since it rules out the possibility of having knowledge of the true limit or functional relation between the variables.

This completes our solution of the general problem of induction. The unsolvability of PCR eliminates the possibility of a vindication, and Hume's dilemma nullifies the possibility of a validation. Hence there can be no prospect of a justification of induction, or, for that matter, of any other variety of non-demonstrative inference.

4.3. The foregoing proof expresses the fact that, for any sequence of events and any particular rule applied to it, the number of observations which must be made before the rule finds the true regularity or an adequate approximation of it depends on how simple the true regularity actually is. If the true regularity is extremely 'simple' (i.e., highly preferable) as measured by the ordering according to complexity built into the rule, then the number of observations necessary will be small; and, if the regularity is extremely 'complex' (i.e., highly undesirable), as determined by the rule, then the number of observations will be quite large. Different rules thus represent different general views about the simplicity of the laws of nature, and, conversely, systems of laws differing in complexity represent different possible worlds, such that in each world different rules work best. Given a knowledge of a particular world, we can decide what rule works best in this world, and, given a particular rule which works best for a certain world, we can use it to acquire a knowledge of the laws governing that world. The latter is simply the problem of science. In the problem of induction, however, we know neither the character of the world nor the rule best suited to obtain knowledge of it, and yet we are asked to justify the choice of a rule. It is not surprising, then, that no justification is possible.

One further point is worth noticing. The above proof explicates what is true and what is false in the often-heard remark that the laws of nature must be simple—not too complicated or hidden too deeply—in order for science to be able to uncover them. The true half of this half-truth can be put as follows: Relative to O_s, the laws of nature cannot be too complicated, or else too many observations will be required in order to find them. And, in general, relative to any particular O_i the laws of nature must be sufficiently 'simple'—they cannot be too far up on O_i's complexity hierarchy—otherwise the period of time needed to collect the necessary observations will be too great for science to discover these laws or to find a reasonable approximation of them. On the other hand, the false half of this half-truth is this: it is not the case, as this remark claims, that natural laws can be too complicated in any absolute sense. No matter what form of complexity they embody, there is at least one rule with an ordering or c_n such that it ranks hypotheses describing regularities with this form of complexity as a very early preference; that is, it ranks them sufficiently low so that science can discover them in a reasonable length of time or discover good approximations soon enough.

4.4. We may ask how general the foregoing proof is. One way to pose this question is to ask whether the proved impossibility of justifying induction applies to immortal observers as well as mortal ones. Let us imagine a godlike being observing the universe with the sole objective of justifying induction. Since he is eternal he is able to observe any sequence of events, and ultimately, any finite prolongation of a finite initial portion of any sequence of events comes under his watchful eye. But let us assume that otherwise he is no better equipped intellectually than man. Question: Can such a being succeed in justifying induction?

It may at first appear that he can. He must be around when a sequence of events finally converges to a limit within some reasonable preassigned interval of approximation (we may even assume that mortals set this interval), and he must witness the convergence. Whatever rule he decides to use, if a sequence of events converges to a limit, he will be there when the posits made by this rule become and remain accurate to the predetermined degree. Hence he will eventually witness inductive posits become and remain accurate to the predetermined degree in the case of any sequence possessing a limit. It thus appears as if the only thing which stands in the way of men justifying induction, or some other rule should one ultimately prove better, is their mortality. If this is so, it would constitute a limitation on the generality of the previous proof, though, of course, not in any sense a practical one. Even though this question is purely theoretical, it is worth answering just to show why no such limitation exists and why the proof we have given is fully general.

Suppose our mythical being is examining a particular sequence of events which is, in fact, convergent. Suppose, further, that he has a predetermined choice of e, whatever it may be. At any point at which he may wish to construct a justification of a rule of non-demonstrative inference, he has observed only a finite initial portion $e_1, e_2, \ldots, e_n$

of the infinite sequence of events. Let $e_{n-k}, \ldots, e_{n-2}, e_{n-1}, e_n$ be the *terminal part* of the sequence under investigation, and let k be any finite value, regardless of its magnitude. We may take it that the values which our mythical being's rule posits as estimates of the limit of the sequence have been within the interval of approximation (set at the outset by the choice of e) throughout this terminal part. We may even suppose that, in actuality, he has achieved convergence and that no other rule could have achieved convergence with a smaller number of observations. Nevertheless, our mythical being is not in a position to demonstrate that his rule is preferable to all others or even expedient! The reason he is unable to demonstrate this is that, for any rule and any initial portion of a sequence, there are infinitely many describable continuations such that the values given by the chosen rule fall outside the interval of approximation throughout these continuations. Thus, though our mythical being's estimates have been sufficiently accurate throughout the terminal part of the initial portion of the sequence and though k may have been astronomically high, he can, in principle, have no way of telling whether his estimates will remain within the interval in the actual continuation of the sequence (by the proof in the previous section). Since our mythical being can thus never establish that the 'convergence' he is witnessing is not spurious, he is no more able to justify induction than are his mortal brethren.

4.5. At this point it is natural to inquire about the relation between the old problem of induction and what Goodman calls "the new riddle." It is quite profitable to do so because, as we shall see, their relation taken together with the solution just presented clarifies the way to approach the new problem.

For Goodman there is only the problem of characterizing the hypotheses actually confirmed by an evidence-set or the problem of systematically determining which projections from an evidence-set constitute valid inductions. He construes the problem as that of explicating the concepts of *lawlike statement* and *valid induction*. The difficulty which constitutes a major obstacle to such an explication is that, on any given evidence-set consisting of observations each of which is a positive instance of a hypothesis of the form "All P's are Q," present formulations of the relations *confirmed by* and *validly projectable from* fail to preclude the projection of a virtually unlimited class of hypotheses each incompatible with the others in the sense that for any two hypotheses there is an unknown event of the same type as those in the evidence-set for which they offer inconsistent predictions. Goodman's method for constructing such a class of hypotheses for a given evidence-set has been described in the preceding pages.

Goodman suggests that, to avoid this difficulty and to refine the notions of confirmation and projectability, we should make use of the entire stock of empirical knowledge we have at our disposal. The whole body of accepted projections thus becomes the basis on which the explication of these notions is to be accomplished. He makes a point of noting explicitly that this suggestion is not question-begging. If the problem at hand were the old riddle, the employment of knowledge gained by previous inductions to establish a criterion for valid inductions would indeed beg the question. But, Goodman argues, the problem is not the old one, and thus it would unnecessarily tie our hands at the very outset to disregard such knowledge because we mistakenly fear that using it would involve a *petitio principii.* Avoiding the use of this knowledge is just a bad habit we got into in connection with the old problem.

The relation between the old and new riddles can be put in this way: Taking PCR as a problem of justification, we have the old problem which has just been solved, whereas, taking PCR as a problem of explication, we have Goodman's new problem for which he proposes intrenchment as a putative solution. Thus the difference between them is, as Goodman claims, that the new problem is a problem of explication and thus not only allows but definitely requires us to use empirical knowledge, while the old problem, being one of justification, excludes such knowledge. If using past projections were eschewed in attempting to deal with the new problem, there would be no cases in terms of which to explicate the concepts *lawlike statement* and *valid induction,* and so no explication at all. This, then, is the relation between the two problems.

But it is easy to foresee an objection to the claim that this is the relation between the old problem and the new problem. An inductivist critic might subject each of the statements in the body of knowledge we would like to use in this explication of *lawlike statement* and *valid induction* to the same projection difficulty we are trying to solve with the explication. For each statement he would construct similar bizarre hypotheses which, on the evidence, are just as well confirmed as the statement itself. In fact, one could choose a bizarre hypothesis for each actually projected hypothesis in such a way that, collectively, the body of such hypotheses would support any explication of *lawlike statement* and *valid induction* whatever. Then he would argue that there is no more reason to construct an explication on the basis of actual past projections than there is to construct one on the basis of any body of possible projections formed from the bizarre hypotheses. If intrenchment were selected as the basis of the explication, we could make any set of predicates the best intrenched. Hence the critic would conclude that there are too many explications and no way to choose among them and that the new problem is actually the old one simply disguised as an explication.

If it is true that in this way the two problems can be shown equivalent, then, given the solution of the old problem presented above, it follows that the new problem is solved, too. Goodman's approach would be question-begging, and our statement of the relation between these problems would be wrong. But the critic's objection misses an important point. It is true that the new problem can be taken in the way the critic suggests and that, then, the two problems are equivalent. However, the fact that it can be so taken does not prevent it from also being taken as a straightforward factual question about scientific practice. In the first chapter we described the work of the philosopher of science as that of trying to articulate the principles underlying the way the scientist employs his skills. In these terms, the question Goodman is asking is this: On the basis of what we know about the practice of these skills, what principles govern the manner in which scientists choose a projection from an evidence-set? There are other questions of the form "On the basis of such-and-such possible (bizarre) practices, what principles govern the manner in which projections are made from an evidence-set?" But there is no reason to complicate the answer to the question Goodman is interested in by insisting that first we should decide in the terms demanded by the critic which question to ask. In fact, the solution we have given shows that we cannot decide which question to ask in the terms demanded by the critic. Asking Goodman's question is simply a matter of choice and answering it is a matter of ingenuity.

CHAPTER FIVE

Concluding Remarks

5.1. In this section we shall examine several replies that an inductivist might make to the argument we have given. Each will be found wholly inadequate, but each is worth considering because their shortcomings may help persuade the inductivist of the fruitlessness of his enterprise and because, in the process of exhibiting these shortcomings, we may be able to clarify certain points which may still be obscure.

The first proposal for us to consider is a reply such as the following: PCR can be solved when it is taken in terms of the foregoing reformulation, as the problem of justifying an ordering according to complexity or a c_n function. For the criterion according to which the preferable hypothesis is the simplest, regardless of whether it is formulated as an ordering or a c_n, is justified by the fact that it is valid a priori. Though it is not analytic, it is, in principle, unrevisable. Nothing we might encounter in experience could prompt us to exchange it for another criterion. Since, in any particular case, it is at least as good as any other criterion, if there is one adequate criterion, then it is the simplicity criterion. Its incorrigibility is, therefore, the only justification it requires.

Let us begin by confronting this claim with a hypothetical situation in which we might expect scientists to exchange simplicity for something better. No one would be much dismayed if O_s occasionally led to the adoption of false hypotheses. We expect this to happen from time to time. But what if we discover that we are consistently wrong, and wrong in the same way, when we choose the simplest hypothesis? What if hypotheses with a certain idiosyncracy, hypotheses of a certain complexity, always prove true? Suppose, for instance, that we are mistaken whenever we draw the simplest curve because the true curve always has a certain wiggle in it. Of course, we might often be lucky so that our data points include enough of those points determining such wiggles to make the simplest curve come very close to the true curve. But suppose we are very unlucky. Does this situation not show that it is reasonable to revise or reject the criterion of simplicity? Why, we are asking, is it that, though we can learn everything else from experience, we cannot learn when it is time to use a criterion which gives desirable results?

For the inductivist to answer that drawing the simplest curve would eventually show up the wiggle, however eccentric a wiggle it is, is quite inadequate because it might well show it up too late. The only answer the inductivist has is that this unfortunate situation does not constitute cause for a revision because using O_s does not force us to wait until enough data have been accumulated so that all curves that are simpler than such wiggly curves are eliminated as incompatible with the evidence. He could thus answer that, indeed, this might require us to wait too long but that there is no need to wait because a second-level induction based upon the successes of such curves would enable us to say that they are the true curves. The inductivist thus claims that no revision is demanded, since, in point of fact, the simplest second-level hypothesis is that the best first-level hypothesis is the simplest of all curves with this wiggle. This, according to the inductivist, is how to interpret situations when we seem to disregard the dictates of simplicity by selecting what is apparently a more complex hypothesis than some of those available. But, further than this, he can argue that those who claim that such a situation warrants a new criterion can do so only because they generalize from the repeated failures incurred in trying to fit the simplest curve by means of the very criterion they wish to criticize. Every attempt to offer an objection, so the inductivist could argue, merely demonstrates that simplicity is already presupposed. No criticism is possible because every objection employs and therefore sanctions the criterion to which it objects. This, the inductivist concludes, proves the incorrigibility of simplicity.

We may grant that a prima facie departure from the dictates of simplicity can be explained as a choice of the hypothesis having the greatest factual support on the basis of a second-level induction. We may also grant that, because this interpretation is always available, the simplicity criterion can be regarded as incorrigible. However, this proves nothing because it proves too much. The inductivist's argument that one can always preserve simplicity against revision can be paralleled for each and every other ordering according to complexity or c_n. Each of the indefinitely many non-simplicity criteria, regardless of the complexity of the hypotheses favored by individual criteria, can always be preserved by explaining away corresponding prima facie departures from its choices in terms of a choice of a hypothesis with greater factual support on the second level. Let O_i be any other criterion, no matter how outrageously complex are the hypotheses it favors. If we are faced with an analogous situation where it appears that continuing to employ O_i will result in worse predictions than we need to make, we can make the analogous reply for O_i. The inductivist argued that such circumstances do not warrant surplanting simplicity but that, when all the relevant factors are taken account of, simplicity is seen to be at least as adequate as what might surplant it. We can say that when such circumstances arise, which will not be infrequent with many criteria, there is never the need to surplant O_i because a second-level generalization can be used to show that the desired posit can be obtained without waiting until a great number of curves are eliminated as incompatible with the evidence. Thus we can equally well contend that, when all relevant factors are considered, O_i is seen to be at least as adequate as what might surplant it. Even the inductivist's argument that simplicity is presupposed in the generalization from the failures incurred in trying to fit the simplest curve can be paralleled quite easily. We can insist that such a generalization uses and therefore sanctions O_i. And in reply to the implied argument that simplicity is essential in performing the second-level generalization, we can insist that O_i is essential in performing the second-level inference from the failures in the use of O_i on the first level. This complete symmetry of argumentation shows that, if one of the parallel arguments is accepted as sound, they must all be accepted as sound. Hence either the inductivist's argument is inconclusive or it establishes that every criterion for complexity choices is incorrigible. If incorrigibility is the mark of a priori validity, then incompatible principles are each a priori valid. Thus this proposal must be rejected because it proves either too much or not enough to show that simplicity is as good as any other criterion.

The second proposal for us to consider here, so far as we know, has never been suggested as a justification. Again the point of departure is our reformulation of PCR as a problem of vindicating an ordering according to complexity or a c_n. If one of these criteria can be established as satisfactory, given the equivalence of the two forms of PCR, we have a justification for the rule containing it. One way such a criterion might be justified is to reduce it to another methodological principle. Of course, this would not immediately show that it is justified, since there might be alternatives to this methodological principle in terms of which a parallel version of PCR might be constructed. But such a reduction, if possible, would offer a new approach to the problem of justifying induction. And there have been attempts to reduce simplicity to other methodological considerations. Any one of these might be transformed into a justificatory argument merely by offering the reduction and the justification of the principle to which simplicity reduces as the justificans.

The best-known example of trying to reduce simplicity to another methodological principle is Popper's attempt to reduce it to his principle of degree of falsifiability.[1] On Popper's theory we prefer to choose the simplest curves because they are the most easily testable hypotheses. To Popper, however, a sentence S is testable if, and only if, S is falsifiable, and S is falsifiable if, and only if, its denial is not analytic and is a logical consequence of a finite, consistent set of observation sentences. This construction brings grave trouble. In the first place, purely existential hypotheses are eliminated as untestable, and so are hypotheses which involve mixed quantification.[2] Second, some sentences which are themselves testable turn out to have a denial which is untestable.[3] But we cannot take these difficulties to be conclusive because Popper may be able to find a way of reformulating falsifiability which evades them and because we require difficulties which show that his assimilation of simplicity to falsifiability is untenable.

Difficulties of the latter type are not hard to find. Popper equates simplicity differences with falsifiability differences by way of answering the question of why simplicity is so highly desirable in science. Previous explications of the concept of simplicity (e.g., Natkin's theory that the simplest curve is the one with the smallest average curvature and Feigl's theory that the simplest curve is the one which deviates least from a straight line), regardless of their adequacy as explications, fail to explain why we should prefer such curves. Popper's answer offers the explanation that simpler hypotheses, being more falsifiable, have greater empirical content and thus give us more information about the world. Let us see why this answer turns out to be unacceptable.

[1] Popper (26), pp. 136–45.   [2] Hempel (16).   [3] Hempel (16).

On Popper's account of falsifiability, a hypothesis is falsifiable if, and only if, there is a non-null set of consistent homotypic basic statements (i.e., statements referring to event types rather than specific event occurrences) which logically contradicts it.[4] Thus hypotheses are falsifiable if the set of their potential falsifiers is not empty. One hypothesis is more falsifiable than another if the set of its potential falsifiers is greater than that of the other (i.e., if the number of possible, mutually consistent, homotypic statements incompatible with it is larger). We shall not attempt a detailed exposition of Popper's theory, and so, in particular, we omit a discussion of the case in which the number of potential falsifiers for both hypotheses is infinite. A full discussion is contained in Popper's book, *The Logic of Scientific Discovery*.[5]

According to Popper, simpler curves are preferable because they are less difficult to falsify than more complex curves. They are easier to falsify because it is possible to refute them using fewer observations. For simple curves fewer points must be determined to put forward the minimum number needed to establish that the dependent variable is not the hypothesized function of the independent variable. Since a function of degree i requires a minimum of only $i + 2$ points to be falsified, $i + 2$ points are all that is necessary to show that a curve of degree i is not the true relation between the variables, the lower the degree of the curve the more preferable it is because fewer points are needed to eliminate it if it is false. For example, four points, at least, are necessary to show that the actual curve does not have the form of a second-degree polynomial, whereas only three are necessary to show that it is not linear. Thus for two polynomial functions, one of degree m and the other of degree n, the former is simpler, equally as simple, or more complex accordingly as m is less than, equal to, or greater than n. The preference rank a polynomial receives corresponds directly to its degree, the lower the degree the more preferable. The justification for adopting this preference ranking is that, simpler curves being more falsifiable, we can, by consistently choosing the simplest curve, eliminate false hypotheses in the most efficient way. Given two curves both of which pass through all the observed points, Popper would have us project the one he regards most falsifiable because, if it is not true, discovering that we mistakenly adopted a false hypothesis is made easier than it would be were we to have chosen the other and were it to have been false.

4 Popper (26), p. 112.   5 Popper (26).

Popper's justification is, however, totally inadequate. In the first place, any curve, regardless of how simple or complex, can always be eliminated with only a single point! For any false hypothesis can be disproved by exactly one point which does not fall on the curve it proscribes or which, given a suitable definition of "too large a deviation," deviates too much from it. Such points can be no more difficult to find than the $i + 2$ points required by Popper's theory because, *ceteris paribus*, locating one point can be no more difficult than locating $i + 2$ points ($i \geq 1$) when one of the $i + 2$ points counts as the one point. This means that any curve, no matter how complex it may be, is as easily falsifiable as any other curve, no matter how simple. Then if we equate differences in simplicity with differences in falsifiability and sameness in simplicity with sameness in falsifiability, every curve is as simple and as complex as every other curve. This consequence is, by itself, enough to show that a preference for the simplest curve cannot be justified on the basis of degree of falsifiability.

But this is not the only objection to Popper's attempted reduction of simplicity to falsifiability, though, presumably, showing by one case that, where there are differences according to the former criterion, there are none according to the latter is sufficient to refute the claim that the former reduces to the latter. Second, there are classes of curves which show that Popper's explication of simplicity is far too narrow, for example, the sine curves. Third, there are cases in which Popper's theory makes simplicity differences disappear entirely. For instance, if we take hypotheses which are statements expressing the proportion of the members of a reference class possessing a certain property in terms of rationals between 0 and 1, then, if differences in simplicity between such hypotheses are differences in falsifiability in Popper's sense, there simply are no simplicity differences between hypotheses of this kind. Take another example of this. The two hypotheses, "All emeralds are green" and "All emeralds are grue," where "grue" is a predicate which "applies to all things examined before t just in case they are green but to other things just in case they are blue,"[6] are clearly cases of hypotheses which differ with respect to simplicity. However, there is no difference between them in terms of degree of falsifiability.[7] Finally, Popper's theory of falsifi-

[6] Goodman (13), p. 74.

[7] A case for a difference between them in terms of degree of falsifiability might be attempted along the following lines: Assuming the adequacy of Pop-

ability actually conflicts with certain basic features of simplicity. Consider a case in which we have two hypotheses to choose from, say, H_1 and H_2, such that H_1 implies H_2 but H_2 does not imply H_1 and in which the available evidence consists of a certain body of sentences which supports both equally. For example, take H_1 as the hypothesis "All philosophical books are abstruse" and take H_2 as the hypothesis "All philosophical books written by Germans are abstruse." Let the available evidence consist of such statements as *"Kritik der reinen Vernunft* is abstruse"; *"Leben nach dem Tode* is abstruse"; *"Phänomenologie des Geistes* is abstruse"; *Logik der Forschung* is abstruse"; etc. Now, if we are required to choose between H_1 and H_2 without the chance to examine such books as Hume's *Enquiry,* Descartes's *Meditations,* Russell's *Problems of Philosophy,* James's *Pragmatism,* and other works by non-German philosophers, we shall choose H_2 because, other things being equal, it adds least to what the evidence tells us and thus is simpler. Yet Popper's theory would direct us to choose H_1 instead because, according to this theory, it is incompatible with a larger class of homotypic basic statements—because the number of its potential falsifiers is greater than that of H_2. Even though H_2 is the obvious choice on this evidence, Popper's theory recommends H_1 because, being broader in scope, there are more chances to refute it. The reason Popper's theory contains this undesirable feature is that it is concerned exclusively with choosing hypotheses so that false hypotheses can be most efficaciously eliminated, whereas simplicity guides extrapolation by a technique of choosing hypotheses which maximizes the chances of selecting the true hypothesis; and these two approaches do not coincide. In fact, the most efficient way of eliminating false hypotheses is quite an inefficient way of finding true ones. In the case just considered,

---

per's account of simplicity as falsifiability for curves, someone might point out that, if we were to plot these two hypotheses on a coordinate system whose x-axis represents the individual emeralds in their order of examination and whose y-axis represents the various common colors—blue, green, red, yellow, etc.—then the former hypothesis would appear as a linear function, while the latter would appear as a step function. He might thus argue that, by this transposition, such cases can be brought under Popper's theory. Unfortunately, however, this type of transposition is not unique. If, instead of placing designations for the common colors along the y-axis, we put suitably chosen Goodmanian predicates—"grue," "bleen," "whed," etc.—then the hypothesis "All emeralds are grue" is the linear function, while the hypothesis "All emeralds are green" is the step function. In this version the Goodmanian hypothesis has the simpler transposed form.

the hypothesis "All books are abstruse" or "All things are abstruse" are each a bétter choice on Popper's theory. Since there are indefinitely many hypotheses which are preferable to H_2 for Popper, a rule employing his notion of simplicity would not even be convergent.

A variant of Popper's suggestion that the reason simpler hypotheses are preferable is that they have greater empirical content and thus provide more information about the world has recently been proposed by Quine as an advantage of simplicity. Quine makes no attempt to use this supposed advantage in a justificatory argument for induction, but we may treat his argument in this way as we have done in the case of Popper's attempted reduction. Quine writes:

> One incidental benefit of simplicity than can escape notice is that it tends to enhance a theory's scope—its richness in observable consequences. For, let θ be a theory, and let C be the class of all the testable consequences of θ. The theory θ will have been suggested to us by some set K of prior observations, a subclass of C. In general, the simpler θ is, the smaller the sample K of C that will have sufficed to suggest θ. To say this is just to repeat the earlier remark: that simplicity is what guides extrapolation. But the relationship can also be described in inverted form: given K, the simpler θ is, the more inclusive C will tend to be. Granted, subsequent checking on C may do away with θ; meanwhile the gain in scope is there.[8]

Quine's remarks do not offer an independent methodological justification for preferring the simplest hypothesis because they are simply wrong. Simplicity cannot, in general, enhance the scope of a theory or a hypothesis by increasing the set of its testable consequences. In any reasonable sense of "theory" or "hypothesis," either there will be statements formulated in terms of real or complex functions and differential equations or, taking the limitations of discrimination in direct observation into consideration, there will be statements formulated in terms of functions whose values are rational numbers. Consequently, the number of predictions or observable consequences which follow from a theory or hypothesis will have the power of the continuum in the former instance and will be denumerably infinite in the latter. Thus given two hypotheses one of which is obviously simpler than the other (e.g., a sine function and a linear function), since the number of testable consequences is necessarily the same because sets of consequences for both are of the same order of infinity, they will be regarded as equally simple. On the other hand, if we

[8] Quine (28), p. 20.

disregard Quine's claim that the simplicity of θ tends to increase the size of C, concentrating instead on his claim that the size of K tends to be smaller for simpler theories and hypotheses, we can easily show that this, too, does not afford a methodological justification for simplicity. If it is claimed that the simplicity of the theory tends to decrease the size of K, then the claim is that the size of K tends to vary with the complexity of putative theories, so that more complex theories require more observations to prompt their adoption. However, this is surely wrong, since it means that, in choosing the simpler rather than, say, the zimpler or the ximpler, theory or hypothesis, we get away with fewer observations for our projection. For a K of any size, we can with equal economy project the zimplest, ximplest, yimplest, or simplest θ. Of course, if, relative to one particular criterion for complexity preference, we consider what determines the relative sizes of samples for the choices of theories or hypotheses of different complexity, then the sample K_1 needed for the theory or hypothesis θ_1 will be smaller than the sample K_2 needed for the theory or hypothesis θ_2 if, and only if, θ_1 is ranked by the particular criterion as having a preferable complexity; for, then, θ_1 will need to be shown incompatible with the evidence before θ_2 can be accepted, and this will require that K_1 be increased by at least one item. But, on our interpretation, Quine's claim is simply an empty comment to the effect that each particular complexity criterion will affect the choices we make.

Hence any attempt to base a justification for a criterion of complexity on one of these two methodological considerations will be unsuccessful. Popper's attempt to assimilate simplicity to falsifiability must fail because these are distinct concepts, and Quine's proposal will not support a justification. But discrediting two such attempts to provide a methodological underpinning for simplicity by no means shows that this form of justification is out of the question. However, if we look at why Popper's attempt to put simplicity on the basis of falsifiability and Quine's attempt to put it on the basis of fruitfulness or economy of sampling are wrong, we can easily generalize from the difficulties encountered to find the reason why no other methodological principle will be capable of justifying simplicity. These difficulties cropped up because the methodological principles involved conflicted for the same case. And different methodological principles will always conflict for certain cases. This is why they are different principles. But, if this is so, then simplicity must stand by itself because any attempt to assimilate it to another principle is foredoomed.

The last proposal for us to consider as a possible reply is one which takes the form of a different type of vindication. An inductivist might argue as follows: It may be granted that no vindication along the lines considered is possible, but there is another line along which a vindication could proceed. This sort of vindication will have the same means, for this is indeed fixed. But it will have an end different from the one of obtaining the best assumption about unknown events. Suppose we try vindicating induction as the preferable or expedient way of achieving the best *and simplest* assumption concerning unknown cases, then, surely, induction can be justified quite easily. So long as you fail even to take account of this possibility, whatever the skeptical proof is, it must be inconclusive.

This proposal merely begs the question. What incorporating simplicity into the end means is that, in seeking the simplest hypotheses about unknown events, we evaluate the candidates in terms of the criterion of simplicity—always preferring hypotheses whose position in this ordering puts them first. It means that we evaluate candidate hypotheses in this way but not in terms of the criteria of zimplicity, yimplicity, or any of the other non-simplicity criteria. But this is surely to beg the question. Moreover, if such an argument were acceptable, we could use it to establish a vindication for each and every criterion for complexity preference. Thus, if the argument justifies any particular rule, it justifies them all. If it is answered that no contradiction results because each rule is justified in terms of a different end—the simplest hypothesis about unknown events in one case and the zimplest hypothesis in another—then so much the worse because we still have no way to show which rule is best for finding out about unknown events. To bring out just how flagrantly this proposal begs the question, we need only consider that, if simplicity is incorporated into the end, then by the equivalence of the two formulations of PCR the end is, in effect, *that of attaining hypotheses about unknown events by inductive inference.*

5.2. Many inductivists reason as follows: "Beliefs are fixed by the rules and principles used to establish them. They decide which propositions are to be accepted and which rejected because they distinguish good reasons from bad. If there were no way to justify the use of one canon rather than another, one would be as good as another, and thus one belief would be as good as another. Hence, if there is no way to justify the use of one method of non-demonstrative inference, one such method is as good as another, and thus all empirical propositions are equally good. Without a difference, there can be no valid distinction. So without a difference between alternative methods, there can be no distinction between good and bad reasons and sound and unsound beliefs." Salmon sums up this line of reasoning nicely: If induction is unjustifiable, then,

> empirical knowledge is at bottom a matter of convention. We choose, quite arbitrarily it would seem, some basic canons of induction; there is no possibility of justifying the choice. They are arbitrary in the sense that cognitive considerations do not force their acceptance. It is perfectly conceivable that someone else might select a different set of inductive canons, and if so, there would be no way of showing that one set was better than another for the purpose of gaining factual knowledge. Yet, such a person would regard certain inferences as justified which we would regard as unjustified. He would hold certain conclusions to be well established while we would hold the same conclusions to be disconfirmed.[9]

The desire to avoid such conventionalism is motivated by the best of intentions. If conventionalism were inescapable, it would be cold comfort to be told that we had achieved the ultimate in tolerance. For, if granting each person the unrestricted right to believe what he wants to means that the astrologer has as much right to believe in his horoscope as the astronomer has to believe in his telescope and that old ladies who read tea leaves in the parlor are as trustworthy as young men who read pointers in the laboratory, then tolerance is clearly intolerable. As Salmon puts it:

> Should we attempt to justify induction? . . . Important questions hang on the justifiability of induction. If induction cannot be justified, inductive beliefs become conventional; if induction can be justified, this conventionalism can be circumvented. Since we need hardly argue the philosophical significance of the doctrine of conventionalism, an affirmative answer to the original question seems inescapable.[10]

But it is simply untrue that these are the consequences to which we are committed if we accept the impossibility of justifying induction. We are no more committed to these dire consequences than is the skeptic to accepting our inductive standards. We cannot argue for their employment, *but* he cannot argue against it.

Let us recall exactly what was shown when it was shown that no justification of induction is possible. The problem to which the general problem of induction was reduced was: show either that one

---

[9] Salmon (35), p. 39.   [10] Salmon (35), p. 48.

convergent rule is preferable or expedient to use to arrive at the best assumption about unknown events or that no such vindication is possible. At the end of the last chapter we established that no such vindication is possible. But this shows not only that induction is unjustifiable but that all other convergent rules are unjustifiable too. Furthermore, another fact which emerges from the discussion in the previous chapter is that some rules are better than others. The laws of nature are of a certain order of complexity, and some of the rules, but not others, are capable of discovering such laws, or adequate approximations of them, within a reasonable number of trials. This is simply a consequence of the exhaustiveness of the class of convergent rules. Thus the skeptic can claim only that *perhaps* we have failed to select the best rule (or an expedient one) when we choose induction. He will have to admit that we need a rule and that we should pick one that is convergent. Moreover, he can have no basis for claiming that another convergent rule might have been a better choice than induction. He can only shake his finger and say *"perhaps* another choice would have been better." Likewise, when we choose to believe astronomers instead of astrologers and choose not to take predictions based upon counterinductive rules seriously, the skeptic can only repeat his warning that *perhaps* we might be choosing wrongly. Thus, rejecting the possibility of justifying induction does not prevent us from preferring hypotheses that are inductively projected from experience, hypotheses which are simplest because they embellish least upon what we find in our experience. But, in preferring inductive projection, we must concede to the skeptic the logical possibility that our choice of inductive projection is not the best choice or an expedient one. We will have to eschew any claim to absolute certainty regarding matters of empirical fact and on a priori grounds at that. But this amounts to no more than embracing the doctrine of fallibilism—the doctrine which all responsible scientists take as too commonplace to deserve mention except when popularizing science and which Peirce took as too significant to neglect even when popularizing philosophy. This, then, is the sense in which the choice of the inductive approach is rationally underdetermined, and this is the only element of truth in the doctrine of conventionalism. One can become an intellectual libertine or not, as one chooses.

Those who have not chosen the way of intellectual licentiousness sometimes try to explain the unjustifiability of induction from their viewpoint. They say that, since the unjustifiability of induction is demonstrated by the fact that all attempts to give a justification end in vicious circularity, the reason why induction is unjustifiable is that it is an ultimate presupposition. Feigl has commented that "the emergence of circularity . . . is symptomatic of the fact that we have reached the limits of justification, that we are at least in the neighborhood of what are called 'ultimate presuppositions.' "[11] Questioning an ultimate presupposition, they say, is asking a question to which no answer can exist, unless it is the answer that no answer is possible. There are no longer any standards to which such a principle can be referred because we have reached the principle that, ultimately, sets the standards. Such a clear terminus must be recognized, for, if something is to be justified, its justification will require independent assumptions which, if pushed back far enough, lead to assumptions that are wholly unjustifiable. To require a justification of every principle means that no principle can be justified. In the case of ultimate presuppositions, then, the rule is: "By circularity you shall know them."

Those who abjure intellectual licentiousness may explain further that there is no compelling reason to insist on a justification. They may say that those who are quite satisfied with induction can simply use it without justification. They may say also that inductive canons govern by the tacit consent of the governed, though there is no ceremony in which individuals give up their unrestricted skeptical freedom in return for predictive rights and inductive obligations. Someone who, quite rightly, claims that we should try to justify induction since the essence of rationality is to try to justify the principles we use, may be given the following rationale: The most fruitful rule of thumb to decide when to try to justify is to attempt to justify every principle or rule you do not know to be justified or unjustifiable. But both the attempt to justify and the demand for a justification make sense only when the possibility of justification still exists. Once there is a proof that no justification is possible, it makes no sense to try, regardless of the alleged consequences. Finally, it may be said that we cannot advocate rejecting something solely because it is unjustifiable because such a policy is tantamount to declaring one's intention to do without justification entirely.

Just a cursory look at the procedures by which empirical knowledge is established shows that induction enters into almost every decision to adopt hypotheses. The whole fabric of scientific, technical, and

[11] Feigl (9), p. 125.

common knowledge is woven with the thread of inductive projections. Thus, from the point of view of our entire system of empirical knowledge, it is clear that playing the role of the intellectual libertine is not so easy as is often imagined. If he is to regard as unsound every belief or system of beliefs based upon induction, no matter how much of what is commonly accepted as empirical knowledge is swept away, he will be left in a position where nearly all the world is thoroughly incomprehensible. What it would be like if every theory we use to make nature understandable were to fall apart at once is something which is, in a very real sense, wholly inconceivable. In this respect, the very concept of intellectual libertinism is inconceivable.

But, of course, those who have chosen differently, if there are intellectual libertines, will accept none of this. There is no reason why they should. They cannot be persuaded, and there is no reason to persuade them. Like a government, rational inquiry will get along well enough so long as the majority share a common framework of standards and practices. The unhappy prophecy of conventionalism is not a serious consideration because, unlike political libertines, intellectual libertines comprise only a very tiny segment of the population.

The fear of the death of rational argument which prevents inductivists from giving up the search for a justification is not hard to diagnose. It is a case of a dual personality. The inductivist is, as it were, a Dr. Jekyll–Mr. Hyde. The Dr. Jekyll side is a personality dedicated to the search for a justification to cure the philosophical world of the ills of Humean skepticism. The Mr. Hyde side is a personality whose perverse standards are those of the Pyrrhonist. Dr. Jekyll is sincerely dismayed by the prospect of not being able to show that one rule for drawing conclusions about the world is better than another, because he interprets this to mean that theoretical decisions and practical choices may as well be determined by an examination of animal entrails as anything else. But this is indeed a peculiar interpretation. No justification of induction is necessary to show that Mill's method of agreement is less adequate than his joint method of agreement and difference; that Keynes's notion of probability as a unique logical relation is far less adequate than Carnap's notion of degree of confirmation; that Carnap's theory of inductive logic fails to deal adequately with the relation between variety in the confirmation instances of a theory and its degree of confirmation; that betting on a horse that has lost consistently because it is "due to win" is losing strategy; and so forth. Something like the process of mutual adjustment of rules and particular inferences described by Goodman is how we show what rules are best and what particular conclusions are best. The problem of induction is something quite separate from this. Stated in these terms, it has to do with justifying one process of mutual adjustments, the one which tends toward the explication of inductive canons, as opposed to another, say, one which tends toward the explication of "don't-believe-what-you-see" canons. The reason why the inductivist takes this interpretation is that the Mr. Hyde of his character insists that, to show one rule is better than another, one must be able to show it to the philosophical skeptic's satisfaction. By getting him to understand "to show" to mean "to convince a philosophical skeptic," Mr. Hyde makes the fearful prospect of conventionalism real to Dr. Jekyll.

The statement, "If there is no justification of induction, there is no way to show that one canon is any better than another," is open to two interpretations, depending upon how "to show" is taken. On the one hand, if "to show" is taken to mean "to convince the philosophical skeptic," then the statement is true but trivial. On the other, if "to show" is taken to mean "to convince those who are in agreement about the basic standards but are interested in more precise versions and their proper application to particular cases," then the statement is significant but false. The confusion between these two senses of "to show" makes the inductivist's claim concerning the consequences of failure to justify induction appear both significant and true when, in fact, it is either trivial or false.

The reason that on the former interpretation the claim is true is simply that *the philosophical skeptic is always right in what he says.* The philosophical skeptic, it is crucial to recognize, calls into question the basic standards of demonstration, not the adequacy of their explications or various applications. He does not criticize them because they sometimes lead us to judge falsely. He is not interested in revealing the features of their applications which characterize the difference between misapplications and correct applications. Rather, he criticizes all applications because they are applications of these standards and all explications because they are explications of these standards. He will be satisfied only if you can tell him what reason there is for thinking a standard is *ever* trustworthy. If he criticizes a standard and you give him another, he will criticize that too. In the same vein, he will continue until you run out of standards. If you tell him that, on pain of infinite regress, we must stop somewhere, then he will reply that nothing can be trusted. If you argue that there have to be trustworthy inferences in order that there may be untrustworthy ones, he will agree but argue that there is no way to tell which is which. If you accuse him of changing the meaning of the word "know" when he asks, "How do you know the standard is adequate?" so that the criteria for knowledge are not appropriate, if he is in a nasty mood, he will ask you how you determine a change of meaning. Whether the discussion concerns skepticism about memory, perception, other minds, induction, or what have you, the skeptic's line is always the same: you cannot know that your basic standards are adequate. But, of course, in this he is absolutely right, and there is no disagreement. However, this is quite trivial because things only become interesting once we assume some basic standard and enter the question of distinguishing good explications from bad and proper applications from improper. What is wrong with philosophical skepticism is that it is always right in what it says only because it says so very little.

Therefore, the cure for the inductivist's fear of the death of rational argument depends upon his coming to understand better the nature and limitations of rational argument and upon his decision to become one or the other of his incompatible personalities.

5.3. It is only fitting that a study of the problem of induction end with some remarks about Hume's own solution. Unfortunately, Hume's 'skeptical solution' has never been taken as seriously as his 'skeptical doubts'. His answer is usually characterized as a retreat from epistemology to psychology and then duly dismissed as irrelevant to the whole discussion. Thus it is only proper that this study try to put Hume's solution in the correct perspective and absolve it from undeserved criticism.

Hume's solution is simple and direct. Whenever two events constantly occur together, this regularity causes the formation of an association between these two events in the mind. The frequency with which they occur jointly instils the habit of expecting the second event whenever the first appears. The more frequently the events co-occur, the more the association is strengthened. Thus we make the predictions we do because the occurrence of an event of the first kind elicits the appropriate expectations in the appropriate circumstances.

This solution, so we are often told, suffers from a peculiar type of irrelevance to which philosophers seem especially prone—it confuses explanation with justification. Hume's solution is thus compared to such cases as that of the psychoanalytically inclined defendant who appealed to the court by saying, "Really, my mother ought to be here instead of me." His solution is asserted to be fallacious, the fallacy is labeled "psychologism," and the solution is passed off.

That it is a piece of psychology need not be denied. But it is hard to see that it deserves the treatment accorded it just for this reason. The criticisms of Hume's solution gain their plausibility from the belief that induction could be justified. On this assumption we feel inclined to ask for more than an explanation in terms of origins. But, as we have shown, this assumption is false, just as Hume himself supposed. If we no longer believe that induction can be justified, we will take a different attitude toward Hume's solution, one which is content with small mercies.

One commits the fallacy of psychologism only when it is possible to justify a practice and instead of justifying it one offers an explanation of its origin. If there is a question, "Quid juris?" one commits the fallacy of psychologism by pretending to answer it with a piece of psychologizing. Hume did no such thing, however. He correctly believed that there was no *quid juris* question, and offered very good reasons for his belief. Thus the critics cannot cry fallacy unless they suppose that Hume underwent a mental relapse in proposing his explanation as a justification and that Hume was too dull-witted to realize that, taken as a justificatory argument, his 'skeptical solution' is easily refuted by his 'skeptical doubts.' But those familiar with the *Treatise* will find this supposition quite incredible.

The proper perspective to take on Hume's skeptical solution is to regard it solely as an explanation of why we make the predictions we do and to stop thinking of it as an irrelevant afterthought. But there is a subtle implication in this explanation which may have been intended by Hume. I do not wish to claim that it is something Hume had in mind, but I have my suspicions.

Ordinarily, we withdraw a criticism of an action if we learn that the agent could not help doing it. Philosophers like to put the point by saying, " 'Ought' implies 'can.' " If we were to be criticized for occupying space, we would dismiss the criticism as absurd because this is something we cannot help doing. Whether or not we take a criticism seriously depends on the kind of act it is that is criticized. Fully involuntary actions, like reflex acts, cannot be seriously criticized. But if Hume's explanation of how the mind forms its expectations about future events is correct, underneath the veneer of statistical sophistication the way in which we come to frame one prediction rather than another resembles reflex action much more than intentionally controlled decision. We are simply creatures so constructed as to be involuntarily conditioned by a constant conjunction of two events. Whenever the first appears, we involuntarily expect the second to appear also. Thus, if Hume's account of human psychology is true, this is no more a matter to which criticism and justification are relevant than is the feeling of pain when one is burned.

Of course, one can argue that Hume's psychological explanation is oversimplified or inaccurate; after all, there are people who expect extremely improbable events because "they are due by now." It would certainly be worthwhile to discover to what degree Hume's theory truly characterizes human behavior and to what degree it does not. Offhand, it would seem that such an investigation would strengthen the general point of Hume's account. At any event, this implication of Hume's skeptical solution is one which clearly deserves consideration.

The philosophical skeptic argues that this merely begs the question because Hume's psychologizing is itself an inductive extrapolation. He asks how we know that human psychology in the future will be the same as it was in the past. There is nothing to say to him. If to believe there is no reply is to countenance conventionalism, then what, we may ask, do those who refuse to countenance conventionalism believe should be said?

Bibliography

1. AYER, A. J. *Language, Truth and Logic.* 2d ed. London: Victor Gollancz, 1946.
2. BARKER, S. F. *Induction and Hypothesis.* Ithaca, N.Y.: Cornell University Press, 1957.
3. BLACK, M. *Problems of Analysis.* Ithaca, N.Y.: Cornell University Press, 1954.
4. BROAD, C. D. *The Philosophy of Francis Bacon.* Cambridge: Cambridge University Press, 1926.
5. CARNAP, R. "On Inductive Logic," *Philosophy of Science,* Vol. XII (1945).
6. ———. *Logical Foundations of Probability.* Chicago: University of Chicago Press, 1950.
7. ———. *The Continuum of Inductive Methods.* Chicago: University of Chicago Press, 1952.
8. CRAMÉR, H. *Mathematical Methods of Statistics.* Princeton, N.J.: Princeton University Press, 1946.
9. FEIGL, H. "De Principiis non est disputandum . . . ?" in *Philosophical Analysis,* ed. M. BLACK. Ithaca, N.Y.: Cornell University Press, 1950.
10. ———. "Validation and Vindication: An Analysis of the Nature and the Limits of Ethical Arguments," in *Readings in Ethical Theory,* ed. W. SELLARS and J. HOSPERS. New York: Appleton-Century-Crofts, Inc., 1952.
11. GALILEO, G. *Dialogues concerning Two New Sciences.* Trans. H. CREW and A. DE SALVO. Evanston, Ill.: Northwestern University Press, 1914.
12. GOODMAN, N. *The Structure of Appearance.* Cambridge, Mass.: Harvard University Press, 1951.
13. ———. *Fact, Fiction, and Forecast.* Cambridge, Mass.: Harvard University Press, 1955.
14. HANSON, N. R. *Patterns of Discovery.* Cambridge: Cambridge University Press, 1958.
15. HEMPEL, C. G. "On the Nature of Mathematical Truth," in *Readings*

in Philosophical Analysis, ed. H. FEIGL and W. SELLARS. New York: Appleton-Century-Crofts, Inc., 1949.

16. ———. "Problems and Changes in the Empiricist Criterion of Meaning," *Revue internationale de philosophie*, Vol. XI (1950). Reprinted in *Semantics and the Philosophy of Language*. Urbana, Ill.: University of Illinois Press, 1952.

17. HUME, D. *A Treatise of Human Nature*. London: J. M. Dent & Sons, 1911.

18. ———. *An Inquiry concerning Human Understanding*. New York: Liberal Arts Press, 1955.

19. KEMENY, J. G. "The Use of Simplicity in Induction," *Philosophical Review*, Vol. LXII (1953).

20. KEYNES, J. M. *A Treatise on Probability*. London: Macmillan & Co., 1921.

21. LENZ, J. W. "Problems for the Practicalist Justification of Induction," *Philosophical Studies*, Vol. IX (1958).

22. MISES, R. VON. *Probability, Statistics, and Truth*. Rev. ed. New York: Macmillan Co., 1957.

23. NAGEL, E. *Principles of the Theory of Probability*. ("International Encyclopedia of Unified Science," Vol. I, No. 6.) Chicago: University of Chicago Press, 1939.

24. NEWTON, I. *Newton's Philosophy of Nature*. Ed. H. S. THAYER, New York: Hafner, 1953.

25. PEIRCE, C. S. *The Collected Papers of Charles Sanders Peirce*. Ed. C. HARTSHORNE and P. WEISS. Cambridge, Mass.: Harvard University Press, 1931–35.

26. POPPER, K. *The Logic of Scientific Discovery*. London: Hutchinson & Co., 1959.

27. PUTNAM, H. "Degree of Confirmation and Inductive Logic," in *The Philosophy of Rudolf Carnap*, ed. P. A. SCHILPP. New York: Tudor Press, 1962.

28. QUINE, W. V. *Word and Object*. New York: Technology Press and John Wiley & Sons, 1960.

29. RAMSEY, F. P. *The Foundations and Mathematics and Other Logical Essays*. New York: Humanities Press, 1931.

30. REICHENBACH, H. *Experience and Prediction*. Chicago: University of Chicago Press, 1938.

31. ———. "Dewey's Theory of Science," in *The Philosophy of John Dewey*, ed. P. A. SCHILPP. New York: Tudor Publishing Co., 1939.

32. ———. *The Theory of Probability*. Berkeley: University of California Press, 1949.

33. RUSSELL, B. *The Problems of Philosophy*. London: Home University Library, 1912.

34. Russell, B. *Human Knowledge, Its Scope and Limits.* New York: Simon & Schuster, 1948.
35. Salmon, W. C. "Should We Attempt To Justify Induction?" *Philosophical Studies,* Vol. VIII (1957).
36. Strawson, P. F. *Introduction to Logical Theory.* New York: John Wiley & Sons, 1952.
37. ———. "On Justifying Induction," *Philosophical Studies,* Vol. IX (1958).
38. Whitehead, A. N. *Science and the Modern World.* Cambridge: Cambridge University Press, 1927.
39. Wittgenstein, L. *Tractatus logico-philosophicus.* London: Kegan Paul, 1922.
40. Wright, G. H. von. *The Logical Problem of Induction.* Oxford: Basil Blackwell, 1957.